U316 Book 4

# SUSTAINABILITY AND WATER MANAGEMENT

Sandrine Simon

# THE ENVIRONMENTAL WEB  U316

Cover images from left to right: satellite photo of the delta of Bengal (NASA); irrigated fields in Burkina Faso (New Internationalist); a demonstration against the construction and use of a large dam in Thailand (courtesy of International Rivers Network/www.irn.org); severe drought (UNEP/Still Pictures); the greening of the desert in Tata Oasis in Southern Morocco (courtesy of Sandrine Simon).

This publication forms part of an Open University course U316 *The Environmental Web*. The complete list of texts which make up this course can be found on the back cover. Details of this and other Open University courses can be obtained from the Course Information and Advice Centre, PO Box 724, The Open University, Milton Keynes MK7 6ZS, United Kingdom: tel. +44 (0)1908 653231, e-mail general enquiries@open.ac.uk

Alternatively, you may visit the Open University website at http://www.open.ac.uk where you can learn more about the wide range of courses and packs offered at all levels by The Open University.

To purchase a selection of Open University course materials visit the webshop at www.ouw.co.uk, or, contact Open University Worldwide, Michael Young Building, Walton Hall, Milton Keynes MK7 6AA, United Kingdom for a brochure: tel. +44 (0)1908 858785; fax +44 (0)1908 858787; e-mail ouwenq@open.ac.uk

The Open University
Walton Hall, Milton Keynes
MK7 6AA

First published 2003

Edited, designed and typeset by The Open University.

Printed and bound in the United Kingdom by The Bath Press, Glasgow.

ISBN 0 7492 56818

1.1

u316 book 4i1.1

# U316 *The Environmental Web* Course Team

## Course Team Chair

Jonathan Silvertown, Department of Biological Sciences, Faculty of Science

## Course Managers

Tracy Finnegan, Department of Biological Sciences, Faculty of Science
Marion Hall, Department of Biological Sciences, Faculty of Science

## Course Team Assistant

Catherine Eden, Department of Biological Sciences, Faculty of Science

## Open University Authors

Mark Brandon, Department of Earth Sciences, Faculty of Science
(Chair and author Block 1)
Nigel Clark, Department of Geography, Faculty of Social Science (Block 1)
Mike Dodd, Department of Biological Sciences, Faculty of Science (Block 2)
Marion Hall, Department of Biological Sciences, Faculty of Science (Block 1)
Stephen Peake, Department of Design and Innovation, Faculty of Technology
(Co-Chair and author Block 3)
Irene Ridge, Department of Biological Sciences, Faculty of Science (Block 2)
Jonathan Silvertown, Department of Biological Sciences, Faculty of Science
(Chair and author Block 2)
Sandrine Simon, Systems Department, Faculty of Technology
(Chair and author Block 4)
Joe Smith, Department of Geography, Faculty of Social Science (Co-Chair and author Block 3)

## Web and Multimedia Producer

Gloria Medina, Faculty of Science

## Software Development

Phil Butcher, Learning and Teaching Solutions (CD-ROM development)
Sophia Braybrooke, Learning and Teaching Solutions (CD-ROM development)
Andrea Goodinson, Learning and Teaching Solutions (Web development)
Jason Jarratt, Learning and Teaching Solutions (CD-ROM development)
Ross Mackenzie, Learning and Teaching Solutions (Web development)
Gloria Medina, Faculty of Science (Software Production Manager and academic liaison)
Trent Williams, Learning and Teaching Solutions (Web development)
Damion Young, Learning and Teaching Solutions (CD-ROM and Web development)

## Editors

Sheila Dunleavy
Ian Nuttall
Bina Sharma
Dick Sharp

## Graphic Design

Sue Dobson
Carl Gibbard
David Winter

## BBC/OU Production Centre

Sarah Carr BBC OU Production Centre (Block 3 CD-ROM)
Sue Nuttall (Video for CD-ROM)
Rissa de la Paz (Block 4 CD-ROM)
Amanada Willett (Blocks 3 CD-ROM)
Darren Wycherley (Blocks 1 and 4 CD-ROMs)

## Picture Researchers

Sylvan Bentley
Lydia Eaton
Deanna Plummer

## Other Contributors

Gary Alexander, Department of Telematics, Faculty of Technology (Block 4)
John Baxter, Faculty of Science (Community Interactions)
Roger Blackmore, Faculty of Technology (Day School, Project, activities for Block 1)
Gloria Medina (activities for Blocks 1 to 4)
Richard Treves, Faculty of Technology (Block 1)

## Consultants

Claire Appleby, Open University Associate Lecturer (Block 4)
Hilary Denny, Open University Associate Lecturer (Associate Lecturer recruitment,
training and support, design of, and materials for, End-of-Course Assessment and Day School)
Sarah Hardy (ECA)
Alex Kirby, BBC News Online environment correspondent (activities for Block 3)
Bob MacQueen, Open University Associate Lecturer (Reader)
Jean Macqueen (Indexer)
Steve Millar, Open University Associate Lecturer (Reader)
Donal O'Donnell, Open University Associate Lecturer (Reader)
Julian Priddle, Science Teaching and Education Partnership (Block 1)

## External Assessors

Professor Sandy Crosbie, Faculty of Science and Engineering,
University of Edinburgh (Course Assessor)
Dr Christopher Hope, Judge Institute of Management Studies, University of Cambridge (Block 3)
Dr John Shears, British Antarctic Survey, Cambridge (Block 1)
Mr David Streeter, School of Biological Sciences, University of Sussex (Block 2)
Dr Caroline Sullivan, Centre for Ecology and Hydrology at Wallingford, Oxfordshire (Block 4)

# Contents

# Chapter 1 Discovering water

**Prepared for the course team by Sandrine Simon**

## 1.1 Introduction

Water has not always received as much publicity as issues such as biodiversity or climate change. However, since the end of the 20th century, water has become a more prominent environmental issue on both political and economic agendas, as well as in the public arena.

For example, 1981–1990 was dedicated as the International Drinking Water and Sanitation Decade, and 2003 as the International Year of Freshwater; various business interests already see water markets as a real source of 'blue gold'; and the resolution and prevention of water conflicts are a growing concern for long term social economic and ethical security — **environmental security** — in many parts of the world.

When skimming through the (increasingly abundant) literature and newspaper articles on water, your attention may be captured by quotes such as the following:

> Water, like energy in the 1970s, will probably become the most critical natural resource issue of the 21st century.

(Koudstaal et al., 1992)

> The wars of the 21st century will be over water, not oil.

(Serageldin, cited in Ohlsson, 1985)

The quotes above are representative of many others that have surfaced at the beginning of the 21st century. It may come as a surprise, but your study of water, this tasteless, odourless and colourless natural resource, should help you question your understanding of what constitutes an environmental crisis and how best to address it. The water that is 'invisible', in our bodies, our food and used in manufacturing for example, constitutes a huge proportion of the water that is available to us. So, it is crucial that all sources of water are identified and 'visualized', if we can even begin to manage this vital resource better. All life on Earth depends on this recognition!

In this block, we take you into the realm of what has been described as the 'blue revolution' (Calder, 1999). Why *revolution*? Perhaps because water can be considered the 'humbling natural resource' that can change our way of thinking about how we envisage the management of our natural environment. Thus:

1    For much of human history, water has not been considered as precious as materials such as gold and oil, but in fact it is even more precious — without it, we die.

2    Although many of our modern health concerns (such as allergies or the decrease in human fertility etc.) are generated by substances such as chemicals and pesticides (etc.), we tend to forget that the biggest killers in our 21st Century societies remain water-related diseases.

3    The right to water is a right to life. Since water is crucial for economic development, its fair allocation and distribution has ethical and political implications.

4    Having water does not imply that it can be safely used; it cannot if the water is polluted and this is true in European countries as well as in the developing world. There is a global interdependency for safe water resources. The ways in which these resources are exchanged and managed will either promote peace and sustainable economies, or water disputes and wars.

5    The quantity of water available on planet Earth is shared between humans and ecosystems. The ways in which one country manages and exchanges this natural resource impact on other countries' welfare and the functioning of ecosystems.

6    The need for international recognition of the importance of sustainable water management is intimately related to the need to value it and learn from local sustainable water management practices. To this end, new forms of water governance will have to be implemented.

These issues will be explored in this book and its related activities.

Implicit in point 6 above, is the fact that *water management* starts at home. Improving water goes hand in hand with *valuing* it more highly. Unfortunately, in countries such as the UK which have a lot of water, people tend to forget just how precious this water is. It is usually only when we are is deprived of it that we realize just how vital it is.

In many dry countries where Islam is practised, during the fasting month of Ramadan Muslims do not drink between dawn and dusk. If you have ever tried such a fast, you will have cause to remember the value of water. Imagine a situation in which, on top of not drinking, you also had to stop all direct uses of water. Life would become very unpleasant if simple everyday tasks like washing anything, including yourself, were

## Box 1.1  A few striking statistics on water

*Virtual water …*

- Importing a tonne of wheat is equivalent, in terms of the water needed for its production, to importing 1000 tonnes of water.

- It takes an average 380 000 litres of water to produce a car.

- 40% of the world's population live in international river basins.

- Water use has grown by a factor of 35 in the last 300 years.

*or virtually no water?*

- 1.1 billion people do not have access to safe drinking water.

- In developing countries, 80% of diseases and one-third of all deaths are caused by contaminated water.

- The average consumption of water per capita per day is 100 litres in developed countries against only 10 litres in developing countries.

- By 2025, two-thirds of the world's population will live in conditions of **water stress\***.

*A state of water stress exists when there is less than 1 700 cubic metres of water per person per year for all major functions — domestic, industrial, agricultural, and natural ecosystems — and the condition becomes severe when there is less than 1 000 cubic metres per capita.

not possible. The indirect consequences of these rather painful restrictions would include not being able to produce anything — food, beer, meat, even cars and paper! Box 1.1 illustrates the importance of water from different perspectives.

The sort of information given in Box 1.1 implies that, while in some parts of the world people rely on an ever increasing consumption of water, elsewhere people either naturally lack this resource or are deprived of it by 'thirstier' economies. The unequal geographical distribution of this natural resource is therefore not the only characteristic of water problems. As outlined above, another problem involves deciphering just who benefits from, and uses, the available resources: these are important economic and political considerations.

Water is important to us at different geographical and temporal scales. In effect, water issues and problems spread over places (trans-boundary pollution, for instance) and time (one can observe water consumption trends, for instance, or the adaptation of aquatic ecosystems to disruptions over time). Figure 1.1 represents the geographical dimension of some of the main statistics relating to water uses, simply by helping you locate these uses on a world map. The figure also shows where there are water shortages and surpluses in the world.

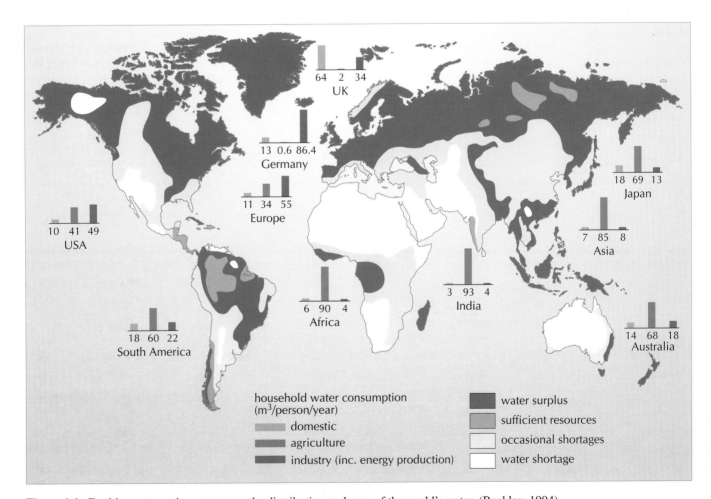

**Figure 1.1** Earth's most precious resource: the distribution and uses of the world's water. (Buckley, 1994)

Figure 1.1 will have confirmed much of what you already know about water, e.g. most of the African continent suffers from water shortages while very large areas in Latin America are very rich in water resources. Considering the use of water for economic activities, Figure 1.1 shows that agriculture is the activity that relies most on water (on average, at the world level). Analysing the two types of information together, from a geographical perspective, becomes particularly interesting and might trigger a few questions in your minds. The map seems to suggest some potential paradoxes: for instance, some of the areas of the world where the proportion of water used in agriculture is highest, are also those where there is a heavy reliance on irrigation* since annual rainfall is not sufficient for the cultivation of the chosen crops. In fact, water experts have shown that there is a high level of water loss in current irrigation systems. Furthermore, many of the poorer countries that grow irrigated crops are doing so specifically for export to more economically developed countries. This water is desperately needed by these developing countries for their own economic activities, but there is not enough water left for such development because it has largely been 'exported' through agricultural products already. These preliminary observations emphasize the fact that water problems are very much related to the allocation and management of the resource.

We will explore these issues in more depth later in this book. For now, simply remember that, at a global level, there are major contrasts in the ways in which water is used and distributed around the world. The water crisis many countries are now experiencing, is very much related to how and where the water is used, and to who benefits from it.

You might have seen television programmes or read newspaper or Web articles that describe the water crisis in much more detail than this map. From the various representations of water problems, one can derive two important messages.

### 1    *Water problems are related to other environmental problems*

We have begun 'waking up to climate change' (Block 3) because some of the consequences are starting to become apparent. The most immediate consequence of climate change, however, involves problems with water, either in excess due to flooding, or in deficit from drought. These problems jeopardize the survival of millions of people on our planet.

### 2    *Water problems have various dimensions*

Although we often concentrate on problems related to water scarcity, political and economic factors, such as the unequal and unfair distribution or pricing of water and disputes over its uses, are also contributing to a global water crisis.

This course focuses on interdisciplinary and sustainable approaches to environmental responses. For this reason, in this book, we will help you discover the importance of water by emphasizing the variety of water responses (rather than *problems*) that have been developed.

This chapter will concentrate on various global initiatives to tackle the water crisis in order to underline the complexity of the issues and problems in this area.

* 40% of the world's harvests depend on irrigation. 60% of the world's irrigated areas (corresponding to 152 million hectares) are located in developing countries. (Gleick, 1993)

# 1.2 International action on water

The **water crisis** is finally achieving recognition as an important global environmental, economic and human challenge that must be dealt with urgently. There is an increasing and varied number of initiatives, and water is the focus of discussion in numerous international meetings where local and global water strategies are being formulated.

At this point, one way of 'discovering water' could be to investigate water news on the Web, or in newspapers, or to take notes of how water issues are being described in television documentaries, for instance. If you did so, you would discover numerous alarmist reports about water problems worldwide. We believe a more constructive approach is to discover water issues and problems by paying attention to the plethora of initiatives that have been taken in order to improve the management of this resource. This approach will help you realize what types of problems are being addressed and will also highlight the fact that concrete *action* is urgently required (rather than solely sensational *debates* in the media).

Some examples of 'water responses' are presented in Table 1.1 and we suggest you explore them through Activity 1.1. Take time to appreciate the variety of these initiatives. Let your mind ponder on the input of problems that could have initiated such actions.

## Activity 1.1   Responses to water crises

Table 1.1 gives information about a selection of responses and initiatives to water crises around the world. Use the information provided in this table to summarize some of the main areas of environmental concern about water and the responses to them.

**Table 1.1**   Examples of responses to water crises.

| Type of response | Examples of initiatives |
|---|---|
| Data collection, decision tools | Global International Waters Assessment (GIWA): the most comprehensive assessment of trans-boundary water issues and their social root causes so far, covering 66 sub-regions. |
| | AQUA is a modelling tool for integrated water assessment, designed to analyse long-term interactions between water and development. |
| Campaigns, education, communication | The 'Water Voice' messenger collects a wide range of water-related opinions and experiences, primarily from people who do not have access to the Internet. These are published on the Third World Water Forum (WWF) website that addresses the world water crisis. |
| | The Dialogue on Water, Food and Environment promotes a global online debate among key **stakeholders** from the irrigation, environment and rural development communities, on the role that irrigated agriculture currently plays — and the role it should play in the future. |
| | Campaigns: examples include WaterAid and Blue Planet Project (an international effort to protect the world's freshwater from growing threats of trade and privatization). |

| Involving women | Women's organizations tackle water pollution problems in Uzbekistan. |
| | Women and municipal authorities begin to work together in India. |
| | Gendered strategy offers cost-effective solutions in places where women are forbidden to participate in public (e.g. in Pakistan). |
| Local empowerment | Traditional floodplain practices contrast with large-scale irrigated agriculture in Nigeria. |
| | Self-help credit management groups are used for implementing sustainable catchment management in India. |
| | Traditional farming techniques in Honduras helped to conserve soil and water resources during Hurricane Mitch. |
| Emphasis on ecological functions | The protection of the cloud forest catchment contributes to maintaining the water supply of Quito city (Ecuador). |
| | The restoration of the Biesbosch wetlands (the Netherlands) focuses on the protection of ecological functions. |
| Emphasis on catchments | The Murray Darling Basin initiative is the largest catchment management programme. |
| | The groundwater and River resources Action Programme focuses on water management on a European scale (GRAPE). |
| | Numerous conservation programmes are focusing on the protection of the Danube river catchment (World Water Forum, WWF). |
| Legislation | New water laws have been formulated in South Africa to manage resources sustainably and protect the environment. |
| Investment | Investment decisions are being based on water use intensity in Norway. |
| Engineering and low-tech solutions | Technical adjustments are introduced in dam design to allow for environmental flows (Lesotho). |
| | The fog catchers of Chungungo (Chile) imitate the way in which plants collect the dew on their leaves by creating vertical nets that 'capture the fog' — pipes carry the water to their village. |
| | Water is being recycled again and again using filtering processes in Namibia. |
| Integrated water management | The cleaning of the river Rhine has been done in an integrated way. Various integrated water management initiatives have been promoted by the International Water Management Institute (IWMI). |

## Comment

The examples described in the table highlight a number of areas of concern. The most prominent of these are:

- maintaining a secure supply of clean water;
- reducing degradation of water resources;
- improving water management efficiency;
- ensuring sustainable management of the water supply.

Responses include the need to both recognize the ecological functioning of water systems and to plan within river catchments and aquifer systems. Approaches to management include the need for a participatory approach, encouraging the involvement of stakeholders, as well as increasing public awareness.

When you have finished this chapter, we suggest you read the information related to some of these examples of water responses on your CD-ROM. A wide range of examples has been selected to give you an overview of the type of 'water responses' and the variety of stakeholders that can be observed throughout the world. Some examples highlight the need to deal with water issues at a particular geographical scale, some emphasize traditional local irrigation techniques, or stress the need to protect aquatic ecosystems to meet our water needs, whereas others advocate the creation of new institutions and the strengthening of environmental laws. What they have in common is an attempt to improve water resource management.

The types of initiative described in Table 1.1 involve a wide range of participants operating across different geographical scales. In parallel, the international community has progressively given formal recognition to the importance of water through various conferences, agreements and declarations. Familiarize yourself with some of the main ones — described on a time-line in Figure 1.2. These more formal initiatives attempted to put in words and principles what the initiatives described in Table 1.1 are effectively putting into actions, throughout time. What these various events and texts really tried to do, was to formulate a description of what 'sustainable water management' (SWM) is about, and how it 'responds' to the water crisis. In order to examine what they came up with, let's look at the finer detail of the events outlined in Figure 1.2 for the remainder of this section.

The first UN conference to focus principally on water was held in 1977 at Mar del Plata in Argentina. It was the launch pad for the International Drinking Water and Sanitation (IDWS) decade (1981–1990) which had full access to safe water and sanitation for all inhabitants of developing countries as its primary goal. Although this goal was far from being realized at the end of the decade, attempts to implement it did serve to raise water awareness and to develop workable strategies for future improvements.

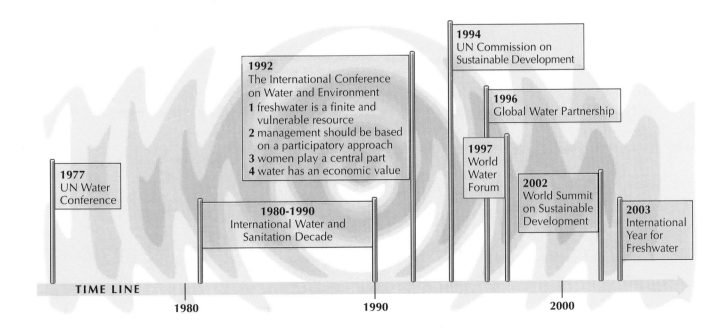

**Figure 1.2** A time-line of selected international agreements, texts and events concerning water.

The next significant milestone was the International Conference on Water and Environment, held in Dublin in 1992, the same year as the 'Earth Summit' in Rio, Brazil (Books 2 and 3). The conference participants recognized that:

> Commitment will have to be backed by substantial and immediate investments, public awareness campaigns, legislative and institutional changes, technology development and capacity building programmes. Underlying all these must be a greater recognition of the interdependence of all peoples, and of their place in the natural world.

(International Conference on Water and the Environment, 1992)

The meeting endorsed four guiding principles:

1 Freshwater is a finite and vulnerable resource, essential to sustain life, development and the environment.

2 The use and management of water should be based on a participatory approach, involving users, planners and policy-makers at all levels.

3 Women play a central part in the provision, management and safeguarding of water.

4 Water has an economic value in all of its uses and should be recognized as an economic good.

In 1994, the UN Commission on Sustainable Development requested a 'comprehensive assessment of the freshwater resources of the world' to be submitted at its 5th session in 1997. This assessment was prepared by a variety of organizations and presented in a report (UN Department for Policy Co-ordination and Sustainable Development, 1997) which gave a gloomy picture of the future of the world's water resources and called for immediate action to improve efficiency of use and to reverse degradation trends. As a result, the Global Water Partnership (GWP) was created in 1996; its mission was to help find ways to put the Dublin principles into practice. The World Water Council, created at the same time, is a forum where all the interests concerned with water issues can meet, debate, reflect and provide solutions to global water policy issues. The WWC organized the first World Water Forum (WWF) in Marrakesh (Morocco) in 1997, where the writing of a World Water Vision was initiated. The second WWF at The Hague (The Netherlands) in 2000, created a platform to promote public awareness for the World Water Vision and generated political commitment to address the looming crisis in water resources in the 21st century. It was closely followed by the International Freshwater Conference in Germany in 2001. The World Summit on Sustainable Development in Johannesburg (South Africa) in August 2002, had a special emphasis on water issues (Table 1.2).

**Table 1.2** The water targets: some of the more positive outcomes of the World Summit on Sustainable Development 2002.

| The four water targets | Current state of affairs |
| --- | --- |
| Halve the proportion of people without access to adequate sanitation by 2021 | 2.4 billion people don't have access to sanitation |
| Prioritize programmes of action to reach the sanitation and water targets | |
| Develop plans for integrated water management by 2005 | 2.2 million people die each year of water-related diseases |
| Invest in water initiatives | |

The preparation of the Water Dome (an event focused on water as part of the World Summit on Sustainable Development) included initiatives such as the Water Matters campaign organized by two leading international UK-based charities, WaterAid and Tearfund. The water targets that were agreed at that event committed the International Community to act fast. Different countries committed important sums of money to invest in new water initiatives that will help in meeting these targets. For instance, the EU, through the European Water Initiative' has invested €1.4 billion for projects dedicated to bring water to 120 million people. In addition to EU funding, various countries committed well over US$230 million during the Water Dome event at the WSSD, for a range of new initiatives. The third WWF in Kyoto (Japan) in 2003, the International Year of Freshwater, focused on water and health.

The recognition of the importance of water by politicians and officialdom provides a crucial back-up and framework of governance for various types of water initiatives, in that it is supposed to help protect both water resources and aquatic ecosystems as well as human rights to the access and use of water. Nonetheless, official texts need to be translated into action. The predominance of market thinking and inappropriate water pricing systems jeopardize the protection of water as a basic need, since the majority of the poor of the world still do not have access to safe drinking water and sanitation. It is widely held that both official and non-official initiatives could and should complement each other better.

From what we have learned so far, it can be concluded that **water responses** have the following characteristics:

- First, many water responses are ingenious and inventive, designed on a small scale by local communities and a variety of stakeholders, and they might provide examples of best practice in the sustainable management of natural resources.

- Second, certain types of water responses can be considered as 'end-of-pipe' actions that attempt to reduce the *impact* of a larger problem rather than the problem itself (e.g. climate change and the scarcity of water that might result from it). But investing in pipes and pumps, for instance, will neither address nor solve the problems created by a misallocation of natural resources (water in this case) due to prohibitive pricing. Other water initiatives might tackle the problem at its source. Thus, the impacts that the improvement of people's access to water and sanitation will have on stopping the spread of water-related diseases, will be more sustainable than that of distributing medicine.

- Finally, water problems are related to other environmental problems. For example, certain water problems can be viewed as an indicator of climate change and thus form a basis for taking actions aimed at reducing climate change.

These preliminary observations support a conclusion that many water responses are being taken to address the water crisis. Examining their variety highlights the general characteristics of such actions and gives an insight into the types of water problems that need to be addressed. Whether these water initiatives will be sufficient and whether they are appropriate is a valid question. The water crisis is still spreading and encompasses a series of problems that are outlined in the following section.

## 1.3 An overview of global water-related problems

Examining the various types of water responses in the previous section will have given you an appreciation of the different types of water problems occuring at different geographical scales for different stakeholders. Here we are going to concentrate on global water-related problems. First, you will examine the various types of water problems that exist in different parts of the world. Then, you will critically evaluate your data using statistics and maps on water availability and scarcity. Finally, you will examine examples of competition for water and of water disputes to see how the main global water problems are linked to each other.

## 1.3.1  The variety of water problems around the world

The summer of 2002 in the UK was wet, unlike the beautiful summer of 1995 when many people found it too hot to sleep at night and there were hose pipe bans and other restrictions on water use throughout the UK. Such severe droughts are rare in the UK, where we joke about being impatient for global warming to bless our islands with a pleasant, warm–temperate climate. The unpredictability of British weather, bringing floods one year and comparative drought the next, is another cause for complaint. In the UK we certainly cannot complain, however, that we do not have enough water to survive. Though we do have problems of water pollution affecting natural habitats, as well as problems arising both from the privatization of water and poor management of water resources generally, the UK's problems are relatively minor on a global scale. Activity 1.2 surveys a sample of water-related problems from around the world.

### Activity 1.2   Freshwater problems around the world

Using the information given in Table 1.3, summarize any global trends in water-related issues that are apparent to you. Do some issues appear to be more of a regional concern?

**Table 1.3**   Freshwater problems around the world. Adapted from UNEP (2000, 2002).

**Africa**

Water scarcity is common — by 2025, it is expected that water abstractions will have risen by 54%. Access to safe water and sanitation is a problem in many areas. Water quality is deteriorating. The major threats are **eutrophication**, pollution, proliferation of invasive plants, salinization. Wetlands, biodiversity and forests are all dwindling.

**Asia and the Pacific**

An increasing water demand and over-exploitation of groundwater supplies. By 2025, this region will be home to 75% of the world's population. Water quality is threatened by salinization, untreated sewage and hydrocarbon pollution. Deforestation threatens water availability and quality. Dam construction for hydropower will flood large areas in China and India.

**Europe**

Overall consumption of water is increasing; 60% of cities are already over-exploiting their groundwater resources. Surface and groundwater supplies are polluted by nitrogen, pesticides, hydrocarbons, acid rain and heavy metals. Nitrate levels in drinking water are expected to exceed health standards with increasing frequency.

**Latin America and the Caribbean**

Water availability per capita is decreasing. Megacities — in which 85% of the population will live by 2025 — will continue to expand. Water-borne diseases are expected to proliferate. Mining is a source of serious pollution of water in several of the countries in this region.

**North America**

By 2025, water abstractions will have risen by 15%. Climate change is expected to increase the demand for irrigation water. Water is polluted by agricultural run-off. There are growing conflicts over water rights between different economic sectors and municipalities.

**Comment:**

The clearest trends affecting all regions are large increases in water use together with decreases in water quality as a result of various forms of pollution. Conflicts over water supply occur in several regions, involving dams in Asia and competition between agricultural and urban areas in North America, for example. Water-borne diseases are expected to become more common in Latin America, but could also spread in Africa where sanitation is poor and in Asia where water supplies are also polluted by sewage. Deforestation and climate change are mentioned as contributory causes of water shortage in some regions, but could also occur much more widely. In fact, most of the problems mentioned, including biodiversity loss (see Book 2, Chapter 1), tend to be global rather than merely regional.

## 1.3.2 Global water availability

The **availability of water** is affected not only by its scarcity (i.e. quantity) but also by its quality and by how much demand there is for it. Figure 1.3 shows the global availability of water in the year 2000. Take a look at this map and then concentrate on the key.

Next, pay attention to the colour of the Australian continent.

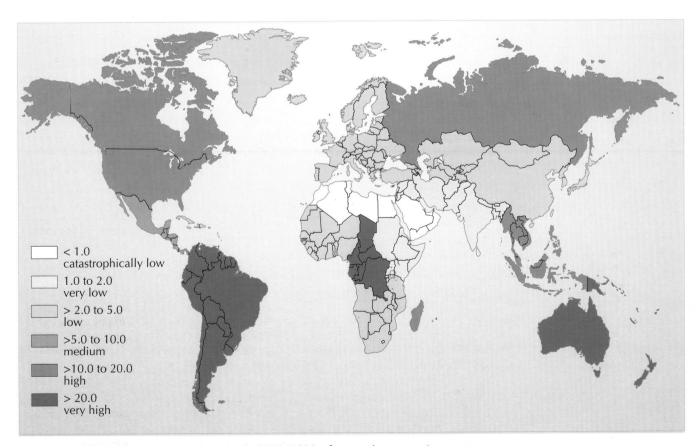

Key:

- < 1.0 catastrophically low
- 1.0 to 2.0 very low
- > 2.0 to 5.0 low
- >5.0 to 10.0 medium
- >10.0 to 20.0 high
- > 20.0 very high

**Figure 1.3**  Water availability by sub-region in 2000 (1000 m³ per capita per year).

● Given the extent of arid land in Australia (Figure 1.4), can you work out why the colour used indicates that it has 'very high water availability'?

● The reason for this colour choice is that water availability is measured *per capita* in Figure 1.3. Although much of Australia is arid, it has a relatively small population (18 million) but a very large land area.

**Figure 1.4** Typical views of the Australian desert: a rock-hole (dried up waterhole) and an Aboriginal sacred site.

This example illustrates the problems that can arise when data are aggregated without the population density, for example, being taken into account. Statistics and visual representations can then become misleading, as in this example where, because the population density in Australia is in fact low, the water availability per head becomes a deceptively high figure.

In order to look at **water scarcity** more precisely, researchers from the University of New Hampshire (USA) have developed a map relating population density to water availability (Figure 1.5a). Highly water-stressed populations are indicated in red; less stressed populations are shown in blue. Maps that use aggregated data (such as Figure 1.3) make the world's three most populous countries appear just fine, when in fact China has hundreds of millions of people without enough water. India doesn't fare much better and some of the biggest rivers in the western USA have so much water extracted from them that they have nearly dried up. The maps shown in Figure 1.5 are therefore a much better statistical representation of the true state of affairs.

Water scarcity is clearly not a problem confined to developing countries and in fact water shortages also exist in Europe, as shown by the data in Figure 1.6. Note, for instance, that water availability is very low in the Netherlands. Figure 1.6 also highlights the difference between the water that is generated within the country and that which flows in from outside the country. In the Netherlands, most of the water flows from outside the country. The way in which water is shared between the countries it passes through can be the subject of serious disputes, as the next section highlights.

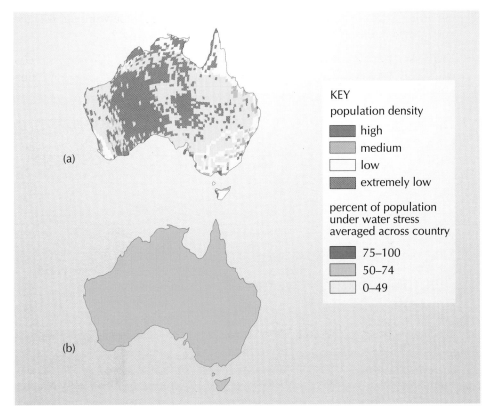

**Figure 1.5** Water stress in Australia, shown using a mercator projection: (a) taking account of population density; (b) not taking account of population density. (Source: National Geographic, 2002)

KEY
population density

high
medium
low
extremely low

percent of population under water stress averaged across country

75–100
50–74
0–49

**Figure 1.6** Water availability and generation in Europe.

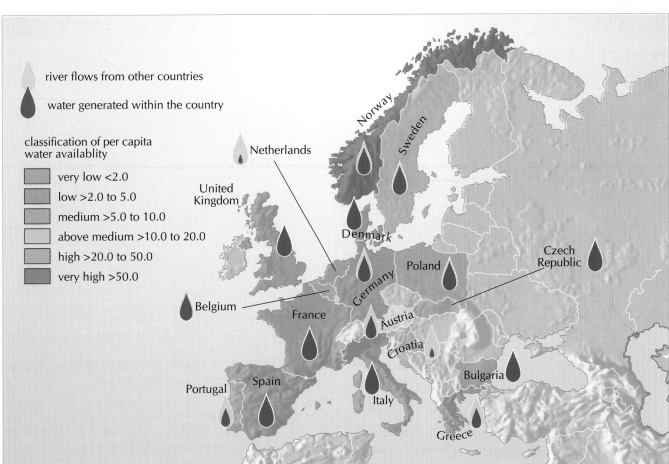

river flows from other countries

water generated within the country

classification of per capita water availablity

very low <2.0
low >2.0 to 5.0
medium >5.0 to 10.0
above medium >10.0 to 20.0
high >20.0 to 50.0
very high >50.0

Netherlands
United Kingdom
Norway
Sweden
Denmark
Germany
Poland
Czech Republic
Belgium
France
Austria
Croatia
Bulgaria
Portugal
Spain
Italy
Greece

**19**

### 1.3.3 Competition for water and water disputes

Water resources have to be shared between various stakeholders and between activities (Table 1.4), some of which are extremely demanding. For example, it takes about 380 000 litres of water to make a car, 3800 litres to produce just 454 g of aluminium and 3000 litres to produce 454 g (1 pound) of grain-fed beef. Each kilogram of paper generated in this course used up about 100 litres of water in its manufacture, and the can of beer you may have after finishing your studies for the evening, will have required 10 times its volume in water, in addition to the water used in the manufacture of the aluminium can. Table 1.4 confirms what you have seen before: on a global scale, of all of our activities, agriculture (with its current systems of irrigation), is the thirstiest on average.

**Table 1.4**  Competing water uses for main income groups of countries. (World Bank, 2001)

|  | Domestic use (%) | Industrial use (%) | Agricultural use (%) |
| --- | --- | --- | --- |
| World | 8 | 22 | 70 |
| High income countries | 11 | 59 | 30 |
| Low to middle income countries | 8 | 10 | 82 |

Our dependence on water for most human activities makes us vulnerable to uncertainties in its supply because, unlike oil, for example, which can be replaced by renewable energy sources, there are *no* substitutes for water. The situation would be eased if agriculture and industry, which consume large amounts of water (see Table 1.4), could be made more efficient by the re-use of water and other measures (e.g. more efficient systems of irrigation).

Where water shortages combine with the unequal distribution of water, humans find themselves in competition for a scarce resource. For example, agricultural demands for irrigation water compete with those of urban conurbations and industry for water supply. The generation of hydroelectricity is another drain on the water supply in many developing countries. Although it is often thought to have a neutral effect on water resources, the evaporation from reservoirs is far from negligible.

When water (a river, for instance) is shared by many countries, the competition between economic water uses is accompanied by a clear political competition for the resource. This competition for water can turn into **water disputes**, or even wars. Some analysts believe that access to water resources — a key foreign policy and environmental security issue for countries short of water — will become even more important in the near future. Currently, almost 150 of the world's 214 major river systems are shared by two adjacent countries, and another 50 are shared by three to ten nations. Some 40% of the world's population lives in countries where there are already clashes over water (Table 1.5). At the time of writing, none of these potential hotspots for conflict over water supplies has a treaty that includes all of the countries within the shared river basin.

Another type of 'competition' for water derives from the different perceptions of the *utility* and **meaning of water**. An ecologist might see water predominantly as a resource for plants and animals, whereas water has acquired a dominant utilitarian meaning for many of us. However if, in many Western cultures, water has aquired the value of a commodity, in many other countries, water also has a spiritual value. Thus, to the African, it is the 'giver of life'; to the Maori, 'a gift handed down by their ancestors' (Calder); to the Hindu, the natural resource in which to wash away one's sins (Figure 1.7). These different ways of valuing water can lead to disputes over water resource management.

**Table 1.5** Examples of water disputes in the 1990s (adapted from Ohlsson, 1995).

| Rivers | Countries involved in dispute | Subject of dispute |
|---|---|---|
| Nile | Egypt, Sudan, Ethiopia, Uganda, Kenya, Democratic Republic of Congo, Eritrea | siltation, flooding, water flow/diversion |
| Euphrates, Tigris | Iraq, Syria, Turkey | dams, reduced water flow salinization, hydroelectricity |
| Jordan, Yarmuk Litani, West Bank aquifers | Israel, Jordan, Syria, Lebanon, Palestinians on the West Bank | water flow/diversion, allotment of water from common aquifers, water titles |
| Brahmaputra, Ganges | Bangladesh, India | siltation, flooding, water flow/diversion |
| Mekong hydroelectricity | Kampuchea, Laos, Thailand, Vietnam | water flow, flooding, irrigation, |
| Parana | Argentina, Brazil | dam, land inundation |
| Lauca | Bolivia, Chile | dam, salinization |
| Rio Grande, Colorado pollution | Mexico, United States | salinization, water flow, agrochemical |
| Great Lakes | Canada, United States | water diversion |
| Rhine | France, Netherlands, Switzerland, Germany | industrial pollution |
| Danube | Austria, Slovakia, Hungary | water diversion, hydroelectricity |

**Figure 1.7** The sacred river 'Mother Ganges' in Varanasi, India.

You should now go the Web to do the activities associated with this section of Chapter 1.

# 1.4 The inter-relatedness of water issues

As you saw in the previous section, it is increasingly clear that the way in which water is managed in one country might have an effect in another. This is easy to understand when these countries share a river, as shown in many water conflicts. When this is not the case, water can still link different parts of the globe together, through what is called virtual water:

> Importing water-intensive products means an indirect use of water from elsewhere in the world. Although this trade in **virtual water** has no meaning in a hydrological sense, it should be recognized as an important issue in a socioeconomic sense, closely connected to the issue of the water self-sufficiency of nations. International trade in virtual water takes place in the form of international trade in water intensive products.

> (Hoekstra, 1998)

Although this virtual link is economic in nature, it very much affects the conditions of life in the country from which the water has been 'virtually' exported; this water is no longer available 'at home', even though it might be very much needed. For example, the water that was used to grow the Egyptian beans on a UK supermarket shelf can no longer be used to grow food for the Egyptian population or to 'feed' the Egyptian industrial sector. Is this a fair state of affairs? This is the sort of question that economists and politicians will have to address when tackling the issues of water and food security in the world, a core factor in the current water crisis. However, in order to address water problems, they will inevitably have to adopt a global, systemic approach. This chapter has focused on water responses and problems at a global level to give you an overview of these issues and to show connections between them. For the remainder of this chapter we are going to focus on interdependencies between the different dimensions of water issues.

First, we will look at the physical links between different water milieu on Earth. Then, we will examine how paying more attention to the connections between parts of the natural environment have helped people envisage new ways of managing human–ecological interactions. Note that 'systems thinking and practice', implemented by hydrologists and others, will then be the approach we will use most in the rest of the book.

## 1.4.1 The hydrological cycle: physical inter-dependencies

People working on environmental issues are increasingly reaching a simple conclusion: observing carefully how nature works and mimicking its functioning through our modes of management, will help us protect both ecosystems and our own welfare. Looking at water management for example, we need to explore where and how sources of freshwater arise, why and how it changes state (from liquid to solid ice, to vapour etc.), how it circulates, what species it can host, what pollutants and in which quantities it can abate them. Many of these properties are discussed when ecological functions of aquatic ecosystems are examined later in this book. You also looked at some of these issues in previous blocks (notably Block 2). Here, we will study the **hydrological cycle** in order to gain an overview of the situation. Our objective is to highlight the existing links between different parts of the cycle, and hence its systemic characteristics.

The hydrological cycle collects, purifies and distributes the Earth's fixed supply of water (Figure 1.8) and is powered by solar energy which evaporates water from oceans, streams, lakes, soil and vegetation. It is uncertain whether, on a global scale, the amount of water vapour entering the atmosphere is equal to the amount returning to the Earth's surface as precipitation, because the oceans are a huge reservoir with effects that are difficult to quantify in a precise way. The main processes (or links) in the water cycle are evaporation (conversion of liquid water into water vapour), transpiration (evaporation from leaves), condensation (conversion of water vapour into droplets), precipitation (rain, snow), infiltration (flow of water into soil), percolation (flow of water to groundwater storage areas), and run-off (down-slope surface movement of water).

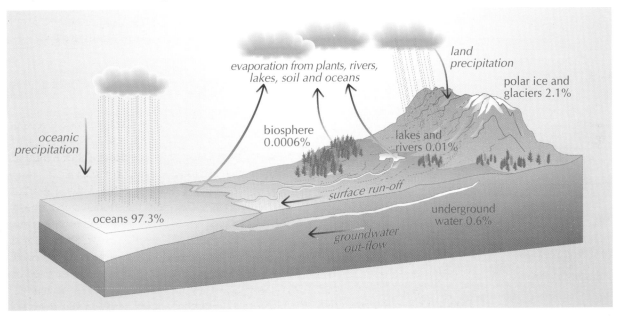

**Figure 1.8** A simplified version of the hydrological cycle and the distribution of water on Earth. (Blue: 'stocks of water'; pink: 'flows of water')

Looking at the hydrological cycle makes us realise that **systems thinking** can help us understand it better. Systems thinking analyses how the different (physical) parts of the hydrological cycle interact dynamically. The hydrological cycle is a good example of a self-contained system; it works beautifully, independently from external forces. However, disruptions inflicted on different parts of the cycle might affect the overall cycle. Since direct human modification of the global hydrological cycle is considerable, the way in which we manage water uses and disposals should be carefully designed to respect the renewal principles of the hydrological cycle. It is to our advantage that water is recycled and hence re-usable. The important message to remember is:

> The biological use of water on Earth is sustained by a relatively tiny (limited) volume of freshwater and it is therefore of much biological importance that this volume is continuously recycled.

(Newson, 1998)

Looking at how different parts of the **water system** interact, as can be done in the context of the hydrological cycle, can also give us a greater awareness of how the economic, social and political dimensions of water issues might inter-relate.

Effectively, what systems thinking can help us with, is to explore how a sustainable water management cycle (similar, conceptually, to the hydrological cycle) can be 'fuelled' in order to improve the interactions between the human and ecological dimensions of water issues. This is what the next section and the rest of the book explores, step by step.

## 1.4.2  Systems practice for water management

Observations of the inter-relationships between the components of the water cycle have inspired practical initiatives that have considerably improved our lives. Thus, in the mid-19th century, the idea of circulation was applied to the flow of water in an urban environment: Edwin Chadwick pictured a new city as a social body through which water must incessantly circulate, leaving it ultimately as dirty sewage. He showed that the city would stagnate and rot unless water constantly circulated through it, being pumped in and then channelled out. This idea marked the beginning of systems of urban sanitation.

Systemic methods of understanding and managing water resources have developed further since then, as shown by the various modelling exercises developed by hydrologists, for example. Simulations and models focused on water and climate-change interactions follow similar principles. The common objective of these approaches is to focus on the global picture: if something happens in one part of the system, there will be consequences elsewhere.

While the systems approaches to water management covered so far are based on physical measurements, other systems approaches have focused on water management institutions and stakeholders, either as systems or as a set of water management units. **Integrated Water Management (IWM)**, for instance, focuses on integrating all dimensions of water management and on engaging a variety of stakeholders. **River basin** or **catchment management** puts a strong emphasis on ecological factors: it advocates respecting the ecological (rather than administrative) boundaries of the catchment to be managed. Other systems approaches have concentrated on creating virtual platforms on the web. These have allowed various stakeholders who do not normally work together to learn from each other and gain a better understanding of the water problems and their potential solutions.

Since we refer to systems approaches and techniques many times in this book, the final section of this chapter will clarify the key terms used in systems thinking. You will have already come across many of these items in earlier books.

## 1.4.3  More on systems approaches

Hoekstra has defined a system as follows:

> ... a part of reality, conceived as a coherent whole of interacting entities (elements, components). An open system is a system which is connected to, and interacts with, its environment. A closed system is a system which does not take in from, or give out to, its environment. In practice, closed systems do not exist.

> (Hoekstra, 1998)

The basic idea of systems thinking can be found in Aristotle's observation that 'the whole is more than the sum of its parts'. In contemporary systems thinking, the same idea is explained by stressing that 'some system properties cannot be inferred from the individual properties of the constituting entities, but emerge only at the system level'. Given its holistic nature, systems thinking typically meets the need for an integrated approach to environmental management.

This book focuses on a systems approach that is respectful of **human ecology*** (Marten, 2001) principles (Clayton and Radcliffe, 1997) — following which, human and ecological systems are inter-related). If we consider water within a system, say the hydrological cycle, we can also view the water crisis as a system. The objective is to examine what affects this system and what types of systemic solutions can improve the situation as a whole. Addressing the water crisis in a non-systemic way, as has been done in the past, generates 'partial solutions' that exacerbate the problem in other ways (for example, constructing a large dam may result in political disputes if people living down stream of the river receive less water).

Systems thinkers (e.g. Stowell et al., 1997) often choose to represent the system they are considering by the construction of various types of 'systemic diagrams'. We will often return to these diagrams in this book and in your web activities. The simplest type of system diagram (a 'spray diagram') is used to illustrate the way in which the components of the system interact. In Figure 1.9 the information about water given in this chapter is represented as a whole system containing various interacting sub-issues. However, this system could also have been represented in a different way; to the system thinker, the drawing process is a way to reflect on an issue as well as a way in which to open a discussion on it. There is no 'right' representation. The spray diagram is merely a starting point; a way to present information. What is of interest to us is the way in which the sub-issues interact.

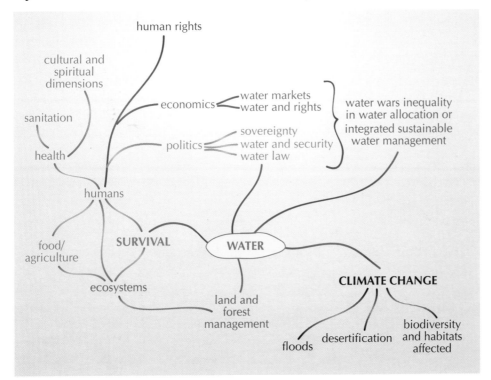

**Figure 1.9** The inter-relationships between the various dimensions of the water crisis illustrated in the form of a spray diagram.

* Also described by some as 'ecological economics'.

In addition to these diagramming techniques, the systems concepts of **emergence**, **system boundaries** and **feedback loops** can help us understand the nature and complexity of water problems. Although you have already used these concepts in previous blocks (Blocks 1 and 3), now is the time to refresh your memory.

○ Do you remember what is meant by the term 'emergence' in systems terminology?

● An emergent property of a system is one which is not readily explainable with reference to sub-components. This means that at any given level of complexity, there are emergent properties that cannot be readily explained solely by reference to a lower level.

○ Do you remember what is meant by the term 'boundary' in systems terminology?

● It is 'the real or abstract delineation between a system and its environment'.

It is now widely recognized that water management should be organized within the natural boundaries formed by river catchments or basins. Organizations such as **River Basins Organizations (RBOs)** have been created to respond to this institutional and managerial need.

○ Do you remember what is meant by the term 'feedback loop' in systems terminology?

● A feedback loop is a circular path of causation.

In a *negative* feedback loop, change is effected in a direction that makes further change less likely; negative feedback tends to damp-out change. In a *positive* feedback loop, change is effected in a direction that makes further change more likely; positive feedback tends to amplify change. Various feedback loops can be derived from Figure 1.8, and Figure 1.10 illustrates one of them.

Because water is crucial to survival, competition for this resource arises if it becomes scarce. If laws and mechanisms for a fair system of allocation of water rights are not formulated to resolve the situation, serious conflicts can result (Table 1.5). Conflicts over resources tend to reduce access to those resources for at least one party to the dispute and so water becomes more scarce. For example, refugees from conflict might have to leave an area and in doing so increase the demand for water elsewhere. Figure 1.10 therefore gives an example of a positive feedback loop. Box 1.2 gives another example of positive feedback, through the story of the water hyacinth.

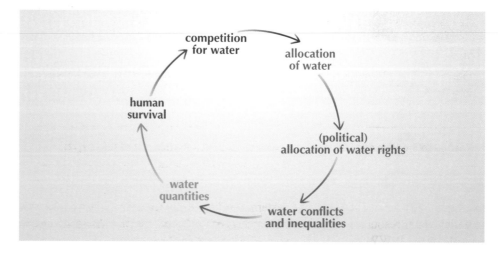

**Figure 1.10** An example of a simplified positive feedback loop focused on water scarcity, that has been generated by an unfair system of water allocation.

## Box 1.2 The water hyacinth: an example of a positive feedback effect

Water hyacinths (*Eichhornia crassipes*, Figure 1.11a) have become an uncontrollable nuisance in many places, including the world's second largest lake — Lake Victoria in Eastern Africa — where fish from the lake are a major source of animal protein for millions of people. Parts of Lake Victoria are now so badly clogged with water hyacinth (Figure 1.11b), that fishing boats cannot move through the water. Thousands of fishermen are out of work, and the supply of fish has declined drastically.

The water hyacinth story shows an exponential growth phenomenon as an example of a positive feedback — a circular chain of effects that increases change. When part of the system increases, another part of the system changes in a way that impacts again on the first part (Marten, 2001).

(a)

(b)

**Figure 1.11** (a) Water hyacinth, *Eichhornia crassipes*. (b) Waterway clogged by water hyacinths.

Now go to the Web and continue with the web activities for this part of the chapter.

In Chapter 2, we will examine how systems thinking has been used to change the way in which water resources are managed. Sustainable integrated water management and the role of the WWW, will then be covered later in this block.

# 1.5 Conclusion

This chapter has explored the importance of water problems for the 21st century and considered both official and less formal water responses available. We examined how systems thinking can help us understand and deal with complex water problems. The different elements of this chapter can be organized in a systems spray diagram, as shown in Figure 1.12.

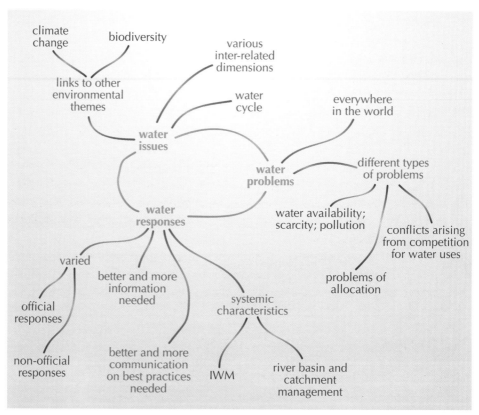

**Figure 1.12**  The various dimensions of water issues.

Systems thinking allowed us to appreciate the various dimensions of water issues and how they relate to other environmental themes (such as climate change). We identified the main water problems by examining various types of water responses and found that there are different types of water problem at different geographical scales. We also explored water responses and realised that these can be undertaken by official bodies or else be much less formal. In formulating responses, better and more information is needed, as well as more coordination of actions. Using systems thinking to understand how the dimensions of water issues and problems are interconnected will help us formulate more holistic, rather than disconnected and potentially counter-productive, water responses.

Water responses are produced to various types of *water vulnerability* that contribute to the global water crisis. The next chapter will, therefore, focus on the concept of vulnerability.

## 1.6 Summary of Chapter 1

1.1 Water is one of the most important environmental resources of the 21st century.

1.2 Events focusing on water and sustainability (First UN conference focused on water in 1977 in Mar Del Plata; various World Water Fora; International Year of Freshwater 2003; Water Dome, 2002, etc.), have highlighted the importance of inter-relationships between natural and human systems, as well as that of water rights and equal distribution of the resource to meet people's basic needs.

1.3 There is a growing number of water responses initiated both by officials and by other types of stakeholders.

1.4 Water problems are widespread throughout the world; these relate not only to water scarcity but also to water pollution, over-abstraction, bad allocation of the resource and environmental degradation.

1.5 Water availability and water scarcity are different. Statistics on water stress can be misleading if they are aggregated and don't take account of population densities.

1.6 On a global scale, water circulates through the hydrological cycle. The working principle of the water cycle inspired the creation of urban sanitation infrastructures.

1.7 A basic principle of systems thinking is that 'the whole is more than the sum of its parts'. Three important systems concepts are those of emergence, feedback loops and boundaries.

1.8 Examples of systems practice in water management include integrated water management, river basin and catchment management, and the creation of web platforms for debates, knowledge sharing and decision-making processes.

## Learning Outcomes for Chapter 1

When you have completed this chapter, you should be able to:

1.1 Define and use, or recognize definitions and applications of, each of the terms given in **bold** in the text. (Question 1.1)

1.2 Describe and give some examples of 'official' and 'non-official' water initiatives. (Questions 1.2 and 1.3)

1.3 Explain what is meant by water problems, using statistics to illustrate your answer. (Questions 1.6 and 1.7)

1.4 List and explain the differences between the main water problems in the world. (Questions 1.2, 1.4 and 1.5)

1.5 Give some examples of water disputes around the world. (Question 1.8)

1.6 Explain how taking account of the inter-relatedness between water sub-issues might help us to understand and address water problems better. (Questions 1.9 and 1.10)

# Questions for Chapter 1

### Question 1.1

Define the following terms: virtual water; water stress; water availability; water responses and water systems.

### Question 1.2

Give some examples of the types of issues that water initiatives focus on and indicate at what scale they do so.

### Question 1.3

Give three examples of recent international official water events. Why do you feel it is important that these events were international?

### Question 1.4

What are problems of water availability caused by in different parts of the world?

### Question 1.5

Give the name of three countries where the use of average and aggregate water statistics gives the impression that there are no big water problems. What lesson can we draw from this?

### Question 1.6

How much water is needed to make a car or 1 kg of paper? How much water does one effectively import when importing one tonne of wheat?

### Question 1.7

What are the main water problems that the WSSD water targets are addressing? (Give the main statistics.)

### Question 1.8

Give two examples of past water disputes in the world.

### Question 1.9

Describe in one sentence what the hydrological cycle represents.

### Question 1.10

Give some examples of systems approaches to water management.

# References

Buckley, R. (ed.) (1994). *The Battle for Water. Earth's most precious resource. Understanding Global Issues*, p. 4.

Calder, I. R. (1999) *The Blue Revolution. Land use and integrated water resources management.* London: Earthscan.

Clayton, A. M. H. and Radcliffe, N. J. (1997) *Sustainability. A systems approach.* London: Earthscan.

Gleick, P. (ed.) (1993) *A Guide to the World's Freshwater Resources.* Oxford: Oxford University Press.

Hoekstra, A. Y. (1998) *Perspectives on water. An integrated model-based exploration of the future.* The Netherlands: International Books, p. 16.

International Conference on Water and the Environment (1992) *Preparatory conference for the United Nations Conference on Environment and Development.* New York: United Nations.

IUCN (2000) *Vision for Water and Nature. A World Strategy for Conservation and Sustainable Management of Water Resources in the 21st century.* Switzerland and Cambridge: IUCN, Gland.

Koudstaal, R. et al. (1992) Water and sustainable development, abridged from a report for the International Conference on Water and the Environment — Development issues in the 21st century, Dublin, January 1992, *National Resources Forum*, **16**, No.1.

Marten, G. (2001) *Human ecology. Basic concepts for sustainable development.* London: Earthscan.

Ohlsson, L. (1995) *Hydropolitics. Conflicts over water as a development constraint.* London: Zed Publications, p. 21.

Stowell, F. et al. (1997) *Systems for sustainability. People, organisations and the environment.* New York and London: Plenum Press.

UN Department for Policy Co-ordination and Sustainable Development (1997) *Comprehensive Assessment of the Freshwater Resources of the World.* New York: Commission on Sustainable Development.

UNEP (2002) *Global Environmental Outlook 3. Past, present and future perspectives.* London: Earthscan.

# Chapter 2  The 21st century water crisis: thirst versus blindness

**Prepared for the course team by Sandrine Simon**

## 2.1 Introduction

In Chapter 1 we looked at a range of initiatives that are being taken to address the impending water crisis of the 21st century. We saw that the inter-related nature of the issues involved makes water problems complex and that systems thinking can help deal with this complexity. The aim of this chapter is to examine environmental problems associated with water in greater detail and to explore the various types of vulnerability associated with them. The water crisis is generated not only by physical shortages of water, by floods, or by water pollution; it is also generated by the mis-management of the resource and its unfair allocation. The unsustainable management of water arises in part from a lack of understanding about our dependence upon aquatic ecosystems. In order to address water problems better, we need to become more aware of the inter-dependencies of ecological and human systems, in other words, less 'water blind'.

## 2.2 Water shortages

In Chapter 1, we reviewed a range of water problems and the initiatives that are being taken to tackle them. Here, we will take a detailed look at specific problems and examine why they make us particularly vulnerable.

The first type of vulnerability is our need for drinking water. We need at least 1.5 litres of water a day. Although a healthy person can survive for several weeks without solid food, a person deprived of water will survive for no more than a few days. In addition to this *direct* use of water (including domestic use), there are also many *indirect* uses of water (for example in industrial cooling processes and recreation). Both types of uses are reduced if water becomes scarce or polluted.

The problem of water quantity is often the first to be highlighted as a typical 'water problem'. There are three main reasons why water shortages occur, examined in more detail in the following sections:

1    freshwater doesn't always occur where or when we want it;

2    the world population is increasing at the same time as the amount of water consumed per person is also increasing;

3    deteriorating quality is reducing the amount of water *available* for human use.

### 2.2.1  Unequal distribution of water

Water is not naturally distributed equally across the globe (as illustrated by the contrasting images in Figure 2.1), and neither is the human population. Unfortunately, high concentrations of water and people do not necessarily coincide. For instance, a large fraction of water is available where human demands are small, such as in the Amazon basin, Canada and Alaska.

Similarly, precipitation is not equally distributed throughout the year. In some areas, rainfall and river run-offs only occur in large quantities during very short periods of time, such as the monsoon seasons in Asia; this water is only useful to humans if it can be stored in aquifers, reservoirs or tanks. Aquatic and terrestrial ecosystems, however, benefit greatly from such surges in water supply.

On a global scale then, people only use a small fraction of renewable water resources, although the fraction is much higher in arid areas.

(a)

(b)

**Figure 2.1** Unequal distribution of water around the world. (a) Areas of severe drought. (b) Lush vegetation in areas of tropical rainforest in Costa Rica.

## 2.2.2 Increased consumption of water

Water consumption has grown by a factor of 35 in the last 300 years, while the Earth's water supply has remained constant. We use about 50% of the global run-off that is available from the hydrological cycle, but this amount is expected to nearly double in the next two decades: growing populations need to be fed. In this context, consider how much water is needed to produce rice (2500 litres of water to produce 0.45 kg of rice) together with the proportion of the world's population (mainly Asian) whose diet is based on rice. China and India account for 38% of the world population and these two countries, together with Bangladesh, Indonesia and Pakistan, account for half of global annual growth! Producing rice to meet the food demand that these growing populations alone will generate will considerably increase our future use of water (Figure 2.2).

There are about 80 countries, with 40% of the global population, that are already experiencing water shortages in at least some regions or at certain times of the year. Water shortages occur because the stock of freshwater available to us is fixed, but our needs and uses of water are increasing. Increased demand is due to population increases and increased per capita consumption of water. In the past 200 years human populations have grown exponentially, so that the world population has tripled in just the past 100 years. However, human uses of water have multiplied six-fold during the same period! Per capita increases are largely due to 'economic progress', which has produced a tripling of per capita water consumption since 1950 alone.

**Figure 2.2**  A field of rice — one of the thirstiest crops cultivated by humankind.

## 2.2.3  Reduced availability of water

Although the stock of freshwater remains fixed in terms of quantity, deteriorating quality can reduce the amount that is suitable for human use, therefore reducing *water availability* still further. Water withdrawals and consumption figures do not show the much larger share of water resources 'used' through degradation in quality. In many temperate zone river basins, adequate water resources are used so intensively that surface water and groundwater resources become polluted and good quality water becomes scarce (Figure 2.3).

(a)                                                                                      (b)

**Figure 2.3**  Polluted water affects ecosystems and people's lives: (a) polluted river; (b) children swimming in water full of rubbish.

Meanwhile, rapidly declining surface and groundwater quality, in almost all of the urban centres in the developing world, threatens human health and ecosystems. Every year, 3 to 4 million people die of water-borne diseases, including more than 2 million children who die of diarrhoea (according to the World Health Organization, WHO). So, having water is not enough: it must be safe, unpolluted water. Table 2.1 gives you an idea of the sort of damage water pollution in particular, can cause to human health and Figure 2.4 refers to malaria, one of the numerous water-related diseases.

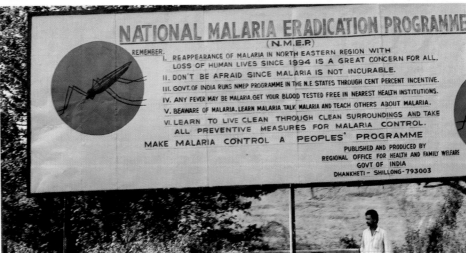

**Figure 2.4** The eradication of water-related diseases such as malaria is of great concern in countries like India.

Water-borne diseases and pollution are not restricted to developing countries; in fact, European countries such as the Netherlands and Belgium are faced with mounting pressure on their water supply partly due to the contamination of water. It has been estimated that half of the rivers and lakes in Europe and North America are still seriously polluted, despite improvements since the early 1970s. Water quality then, may be the biggest emerging water problem in the industrial world (Figure 2.5). Conventional drinking water treatment processes do not remove all the chemicals and pharmaceuticals that enter the water system today, and trace quantities of some of these are now recognized as carcinogens. In addition, leaks of nuclear waste into aquifers and surface water have not been brought under control, especially in the transition economies of Central and Eastern Europe.

**Table 2.1**  Some examples of diseases transmitted to humans through contaminated drinking water. (Source: Miller, 1998, p. 516)

| Type of organism | Diseases | Effects |
| --- | --- | --- |
| bacteria | typhoid fever | diarrhoea, severe vomiting, enlarged spleen, inflamed intestine; often fatal if untreated |
| bacteria | cholera | diarrhoea, severe vomiting, dehydration; often fatal if untreated |
| bacteria | bacterial dysentery | diarrhoea; rarely fatal, except in infants without proper treatment |
| bacteria | enteritis | severe stomach pain, nausea, vomiting; rarely fatal |
| viruses | infectious hepatitis | fever, severe headache, loss of appetite, abdominal pain, jaundice, enlarged liver; rarely fatal but may cause permanent liver damage |
| parasitic protoctist | amoebic dysentery | severe diarrhoea, headache, abdominal pain, chills, fever; if not treated can cause liver abscess, bowel perforation, and death |
| parasitic protoctist | giardiasis | diarrhoea, abdominal cramps, flatulence, belching, fatigue |
| parasitic worms | schistosomiasis | abdominal pain, skin rash, anaemia, chronic fatigue, and chronic general ill health |

(a)

(b)

**Figure 2.5**  Various types of water pollution throughout Europe. (a) Groundwater pollution in Germany. (b) Pollution by pesticides in Italy.

## 2.3 Floods

In this section, one of the issues we will consider is whether the more water we have, the better off we are. In Chapter 1 we saw that human activities affect the hydrological cycle and can contribute to drought as well as flooding (Figure 2.6). Floods sometimes provide benefits to ecosystems; some ecosystems even depend on them. Moreover, some traditional systems of agriculture are dependent on floods for irrigation and fertilization, as was the case in the Nile Basin before the High Aswan Dam was built. However, floods are better known for the devastation they cause to human lives and infrastructure (Figure 2.6b). In the 1990s, severe flooding devastated the Mississippi river basin, and thousands of lives were also lost during this decade in Bangladesh, China, Guatemala, Honduras, Somalia, South Africa and Venezuela. Between 1973 and 1997, an average of 66 million people a year suffered flood damage, making flooding the most destructive of all natural disasters (including earthquakes and droughts).

(a)                                              (b)                                             (c)

**Figure 2.6** Floods in various parts of the world. (a) River Severn, Worcester, UK. (b) Floods in Bangladesh. (c) Floods in Prague.

● Think back to floods that occured in the last few years. Figure 2.6. might bring back some memories. What are the major problems people have to face?

● People lose their possessions and often their homes too. Floods can displace whole communities. They can also carry and spread water-related diseases.

The media give widespread coverage to floods in the UK and many other places all around the world (e.g. Eastern Europe, Mozambique and Bangladesh). In 1988 for example, a disastrous flood covered two-thirds of Bangladesh for 3 weeks: at least 2000 people drowned and 30 million people were left homeless (Miller, 1988). The scale of floods is usually momentous and more and more people are affected by such disasters. While flooding is often described as a natural phenomenon, many human activities contribute to flooding. Over-grazing, deforestation, cultivation and urban development have all greatly reduced the rate of **infiltration** and thereby increased surface run-off. More surface run-off means that less water percolates down to recharge the groundwater supplies and a greater volume of water runs instead into streams and rivers at a faster rate, often causing a sudden influx of water. As a consequence, this higher volume of surface run-off not only increases the severity and frequency of flooding, but also degrades the environment by carrying greater amounts of sediment and pollutants from surface erosion.

# 2.4 Allocation of water resources

So far, we have examined vulnerability related to water shortages. Here, we will see how the vulnerability or strength of people, with regard to water issues, is very much affected by how much water is allocated to them, and by whether or not they can cope with 'water shocks' of different types.

Not all people are equally affected by the water crisis, or equally equipped to deal with it. People in developing countries, have less capacity to adapt to change and are more vulnerable to environmental stresses. Poverty is one of the most important causes of vulnerability to environmental threats: poor people therefore bear a disproportionate burden of the impact of disasters (conflicts, droughts and pollution for example). As UNEP explains:

> There is a large and widening vulnerability gap between well off people with better all round coping capacity, who are becoming gradually less vulnerable, and the poor who grow increasingly so.

(UNEP, 2000)

**Figure 2.7** Water demands in cities are going to carry on increasing.

Furthermore, the rapid extension of towns seems to be increasing the rise of a particularly 'vulnerable group':

> Of the projected 1 billion new urban dwellers by 2010, most will probably be absorbed by cities in developing countries that already face multiple problems such as shortages of adequate housing, infrastructure, potable water supplies, adequate sanitation and transportation systems as well as environmental pollution.

(UNEP, 2000)

Cities are therefore becoming particularly 'vulnerable places' with regards to water (Figure 2.7). Their growing population increases the demand for water while simultaneously decreasing its quality, hence jeopardizing water availability.

All in all, the situation in towns is therefore becoming critical: by 2015, the additional urban population that has to be reached to achieve the target of the World Summit on Sustainable Development (half of the global population with access to safe drinking water and adequate sanitation) will be 1 billion. This is not simply a problem of access to clean water and sanitation: it is also tied up with the problem of poverty.

The infrastructure necessary to supply freshwater in urban areas (which includes the treatment of polluted water), is expensive. Many urban dwellers are not able to pay for safe freshwater. Thus, even in places where there might be enough water for all, in reality a large proportion of the population do not have access to this *safe* water.

- Since clean water, like breathable air, is a natural resource essential to life, is it justifiable to provide it only to those who have an ability to pay for it?

- This is clearly a contentious issue. Having access to water should be considered a human right so that people should not be penalized by prices. However, the infrastructure necessary for the supply and treatment of water is expensive, so who is to foot the bill?

The way forward is to identify the cost of water services and mobilize the funds necessary to provide these. As stressed by the Director General of the Department of Water and Forestry in South Africa at the WSSD, there is enough money to meet the water targets that emerged from the WSSD (Chapter 1). However, reaching these targets involves managerial changes such as the creation of a constitutional framework for local government finance, as well as the integrated management of natural resources. These changes are desperately needed if many poor people, who already pay for water, are to get the minimum they need for health and dignity in return. Currently, they do not. Consequently, many water experts believe that the global water crisis is not about having too little water to satisfy our needs, but a result of poor water management, that leaves billions of people and the environment suffering.

So what is wrong with the way in which water resources are currently managed? There are four main aspects of most current approaches to water resource management that contribute to current water problems. These are:

1      a failure to protect **ecosystem functioning**;

2      a fragmented rather than a holistic approach;

3      an emphasis on inappropriate engineering;

4      a focus on supply rather than demand.

We will examine each of these in the following section.

## 2.5  Problems related to water management

In order to envisage new ways of managing water resources, it is important to understand how aquatic ecosystems function, and how they can be (negatively or positively) affected by economic activities.

### 2.5.1  The functioning of aquatic ecosystems

Aquatic and terrestrial ecosystems provide a number of water-related services. It is useful to distinguish between three kinds of **ecosystem services** in relation to water: Ecosystems provide:

- a **source** of water storage and supply;

- a **sink** for waste which, within limits, aquatic ecosystems may remove, dilute or detoxify;

- a **life support** for various habits.

- a **resource** for recreation and for spiritual or cultural experience.

The ability of ecosystems to provide these services depends upon their natural functioning. You examined this in Block 2. Refresh your memory by answering the following question:

⬤    What is the distinction between the functioning of an ecosystem and the services it may provide?

⬤    Functions are processes that an ecosystem does naturally, such as the recycling of nutrients. Services are what we 'take' from an ecosystem, such as harvests of fish or clean water.

Table 2.2 shows how economic activities impact on various functions and services.

**Table 2.2**   How the impacts on source functions affect the other ecological functions.

| Economic activities | Water source | Water as a sink | Ecosystem function | Human health and amenity services |
|---|---|---|---|---|
| agriculture<br>industry<br>public and private water supply | water abstraction | problems of dilution /abatement of the pollution | disruption of habitats | lack of availability of water; problems of quality |

Heavy demand on one ecosystem service, for example as a sink for waste, can damage the functioning of the ecosystem as a whole and thus jeopardize other services such as the supply of clean water. In the same way, the over-abstraction of water will affect other ecosystem services at a local, or regional level, as well as having other negative impacts on ecosystem functioning on a much broader scale (Table 2.2). For instance, data suggest that 20–35% of freshwater fish are vulnerable or endangered, mainly because of habitat alteration. These types of effects can be described by looking at how some human activities that might over-abstract water affect the 'source function' and how the negative effects on this function affect the other functions and services. In the case of the fish, it is important to stress the fact that the vulnerability of the species might be related to the fact that their habitat is damaged — rather than the fish being over-fished. Box 2.1 illustrates how affecting the source function of water (effectively making the resource more scarce) can also affect the 'human health' function negatively.

## Box 2.1  Water shortages and Public Health

Following the privatization of water companies in the UK, a sharp rise in the number of households being disconnected was observed; it tripled from 1988 to 1994. Critics stressed that cutting off water supplies endangered public health. In fact, in1992 there was a rise in the number of cases of dysentery reported in all major conurbations other than London, related to these (non-notified) water cut-offs.

Water over-abstraction reduces the capacity of an ecosystem to dilute potential pollution. This in turn might affect the quality of the habitat and its amenity value, as well as human health, as illustrated in Box 2.1. Therefore, when humans face a shortage of water, aquatic ecosystems will also rapidly lose their ability to act as pollution filters resulting in possible damage to the habitats. This multiple-effect phenomenon also occurs when the starting problem is water pollution, as we will see next.

## *Water pollution*

Water pollution is produced by any chemical, biological or physical change in water quality that has a harmful effect on living organisms or that makes water unusable for any purpose. There are several classes of water pollutants:

*Disease-causing agents (pathogens)* include bacteria, viruses and parasitic worms that enter water from domestic sewage and untreated human and animal wastes.

*Oxygen-demanding wastes* are organic wastes such as sewage that are decomposed by aerobic (oxygen-requiring) bacteria. Large populations of bacteria can develop in these wastes and degrade water quality by depleting the water of dissolved oxygen, thus causing fish and other forms of oxygen-consuming aquatic life to die.

*Water-soluble inorganic chemicals* include acids, salts and compounds of toxic metals such as mercury and lead. High levels of these chemicals can damage aquatic ecosystems, as well as making the water unfit to drink.

*Inorganic plant nutrients* are another type of water pollutant. Water-soluble nitrates and phosphates (often coming from agricultural activities) can cause excessive growth of algae and other aquatic plants, which then die and decay and in so doing, deplete water of dissolved oxygen and therefore kill the fish population. The enrichment of waters caused by such nutrients is described as 'eutrophication' (Figure 2.8).

*Organic chemicals* include oil, gasoline, plastics, pesticides and many other chemicals that can threaten the lives of humans and the other members of ecosystems.

Pollutants may damage not only the natural environment but also human health. Because the threshold concentrations at which pollutants generate a problem are different for humans than for the other forms of life in an ecosystem, we are not always aware of such health hazards early enough. The ecosystem may have been disrupted long before our health has been affected for example. But if we recognize warning signs in the natural environment, then we can take early action to protect our health, by attempting to restore the health of the natural ecosystem.

**Figure 2.8** A eutrophic river covered with algae.

When considering these issues, a further classification is typically adopted to aid the identification of the source(s) of the pollution:

**Point sources** are discharged pollutants at specific locations through pipes, ditches or sewers into water. Because point sources are at specific places, they are fairly easy to identify, monitor and regulate.

**Non-point sources** are sources that cannot be traced to any single site of discharge. They are usually large land areas that pollute water by run-off, or depositions from the atmosphere.

○ Can you think of some examples of point sources of pollution?

○ Point sources include factories, sewage treatment plants, active and abandoned underground mines, offshore wells and oil tankers.

Non-point sources include for example, acid deposition, run-off of chemicals into surface water and seepage into the ground from livestock, logged forests and urban streets. In the USA, non-point source pollution from agriculture — such as pesticides and salts dissolved in irrigation water — is responsible for about 60% of the total mass of pollutants entering streams and about 55% of that entering lakes (Miller, 1998).

So, water pollution can 'flow' through the whole hydrological cycle. One good illustration of this is **acidification**, which occurs when acid-forming pollutants deposited from the air have adverse effects on freshwater quality. This form of non-point source pollution involves numerous compounds (e.g. sulfur dioxides and nitrogen oxides) and sources (agriculture, transport, industry, etc.). The signs of acidification that we are most familiar with include vast diseased forests in Europe, where trees have been 'burned out' by acid rain (Figure 2.9). Acidification can therefore become a trans-boundary pollution issue, affecting countries located at some distance from the source.

**Figure 2.9** Forest affected by acid rain, White Face Mountain, upstate New York, USA.

● Can you think of some water pollution problems in the UK?

● Eutrophication is one of the main water pollution problems in the UK. Information provided by the Environment Agency actually indicates that the damage caused by eutrophication is estimated to cost between £75 million and £115 million per year. Pollution of waters by pesticides has also been detected.

### Conclusion: human impacts on ecosystem functions

To conclude we can note that, ultimately, it is not only pollution and over-abstraction that affect ecosystem functions and services, because even projects like channelling a river can create damage to the river habitat. The inter-relationships between the functioning and services of ecosystems are at the centre of several water-related environmental problems (De Groot (1992) and Freedman (1989)). Table 2.3 lists some examples, many of which you have already encountered earlier in the course (Blocks 2 and 3).

**Table 2.3**  Threats to ecosystem functions and services from human activities. (Adapted from Daily (1997) in IUCN (2000) p. 44 and WR. Note the examples provided here are only *optional* readings.)

| Human activities | Impacts on aquatic ecosystems | Functions and services at risk | Examples provided in the WR set book or CD-ROM |
|---|---|---|---|
| population and consumption growth | increases pressure to divert more water and acquire more cultivated land; increases water pollution, acid rain and the potential for climate change | virtually all aquatic ecosystem functions | New York case study |
| infrastructure development (dams, dykes etc.) | loss of ecosystem integrity alters timing and quantity of river flows, water temperature, nutrient and sediment transport, delta replenishment, migration | water quantity and quality, habitats, floodplains fertility, sports, fisheries, maintenance of deltas and their economies | Mekong case study |
| land conversion and poor land use (deforestation etc.) | eliminates key component of aquatic environment; loss of functions, integrity, habitats and biodiversity, alters run-off patterns, inhibits natural recharge, fills water bodies with silt | natural flood control, habitat for fisheries and waterfowl, recreation, water supply, water quantity and quality, transport | St. Lucia case study |
| over-harvesting and over-exploitation | depletes living resources, ecosystem functions and biodiversity (e.g. groundwater depletion, loss of fisheries) | food production, sport and commercial fisheries, habitats, water supply, quantity and quality | St. Lucia case study |
| introduction of exotic species | eliminates native species, alters production and nutrient cycling, loss of biodiversity | water quality, sport and commercial fisheries, fish and wildlife habitat, transport | South African case study |
| release of chemical and biological pollutants to water, land and air | pollution of water bodies alters chemistry and ecology of rivers, lakes and wetlands | water supply, habitat, fisheries, recreation | New York case study |
| greenhouse gas emissions inducing climate change | potential dramatic changes in run-off patterns from increases in temperature and changes in rainfall patterns | water supply, hydropower, transportation, fish and wildlife habitat, pollution dilution, recreation, fisheries, flood control | Various examples, e.g. water management in the Dry West of the US |

In this section, we reviewed some aspects of *ecosystem vulnerability* that are generated when ecological functioning is jeopardized. It was also suggested that our health and welfare are endangered in such situations. In the next section, we are going to examine further the extent to which *we* create problems for ourselves when water resources are not managed in an ecologically sound manner.

## 2.5.2 Approaches to water management

In order to manage water resources in a sustainable way, it is vital that all ecological functions are considered. In this section we will look at problems generated by several different traditional approaches to water management in an attempt to learn from the mistakes made in the past.

### *The emphasis on water engineering*

One traditional approach to water management is to employ large-scale engineering to move and store water, and to remove waste. Although this type of approach is still very much in use, it is not new. In fact, Roman systems of water distribution and sanitation are some of the most famous examples of water engineering (Figure 2.10). The construction of dams helped to meet the demands of cities for water as well those of agriculture for irrigation. The Romans also used sewerage systems to move human waste from the domestic sources of its production.

**Figure 2.10**  Roman aqueduct, Pont du Gard, France.

Water engineering projects have the capacity to help us overcome one of human societies' major anxieties: being short of water. They constitute one of the most striking illustrations of human control of nature since they can 'capture' water. Their prime outcome is to provide freshwater and they do so in different ways:

- dams and reservoirs store run-off;
- surface water can be transported between different areas;
- groundwater can be withdrawn;
- saltwater can be converted to freshwater through desalination processes.

Modern water development has long used a simple formula: estimate the demand for water and then build new supply projects to meet it — what is now known as the **supply approach**.

But control over nature has its limits. With the dramatic rise in water needs today, the reality is that water supplies cannot be increased indefinitely. The quantity of freshwater available for human use is limited and even if we decided to use new sources such as freshwater captured in ice, or desalinated seawater, this can only be done at a high cost. Supply approaches to water management do not seem viable in the long term. Besides, and as we saw earlier (Section 2.4), the assumption that a 'supply-orientated' approach will make water available to everybody is failing and, inevitably, it is poor people who are not reached. In addition, within supply-driven approaches, downstream users, especially trans-national ones, are given little weight in the quest for 'development'. This way of approaching water problems still reigns in the water departments of numerous countries in both the developed and the developing world. Career development for water engineers seems to involve an association with large civil engineering projects — the larger the better! Involvement in such projects has been likened to a 'rite of passage' for water engineers (see Figure 2.11).

**Figure 2.11**   The Three Gorges Dam, China.

Another shortcoming of supply approaches is ecological in nature. These approaches were pushed to such an extreme in the past that, in many developed countries, the ethos of the water engineer was to equate efficiency with the maximum use of water for the users. Taken to its limits, any residual flow in rivers was seen as wastage. Water projects that were originally intended to solve water problems created ecological problems instead. For example, straightening rivers and altering the shape of river beds — often done in urban areas because a channel with a rectangular cross-section takes up less space — can alter patterns of erosion and deposition resulting in problems downstream.

Such criticisms of water engineering projects are opening new avenues in the area of water management. It is now recognized that water engineers are, to some extent, the victims of their own success. Most of the world's best sites for such projects have already been developed and the cost of developing the remaining potential sites is becoming prohibitive. There is now a greater emphasis on ecological integrity. As a consequence, the inter-dependencies between ecological functioning, carrying capacity constraints and our need for water and various water services, have resulted in a shift to more integrated approaches. However, before such new policies can be implemented, the obstacles generated by such 'sectoral approaches' will still have to be addressed, as explained in the next section.

## Sectoral approaches

**Sectoral approaches** advocate the subdivision of water management into various tasks controlled by different specialized agencies: the 'biodiversity department'; the 'water management department', etc. In most countries, water continues to be managed sector by sector, by a highly fragmented set of institutions. In order to understand better what is meant by this, try Activity 2.1.

### Activity 2.1   Land and water management: engineering versus integrated approaches

'It stands to reason', said the farmer, 'we've only had these quick, high floods since the foresters ploughed those hills up there'. This man's knowledge of, dependence on, and reaction to his local river made his reasoning easy. Yet to a government hydrologist, proving the link between preparing upland soil for successful afforestation and a change in the **unit hydrograph** for the basin, would take a decade of expensive research. Even then the logical outcome of the proven link between land there and water here — i.e. modifying forestry practice, compensating the farmer or afforesting a less sensitive hillside — would not have been translated into public policy. There are simply no river-related land planning policies in many countries. The outcome instead was that local authority engineers built the farmer a bridge over the newly flood-prone stream. Perhaps it is the tendency of civil engineers to solve point-problems where they arise in this way that has discouraged the 'look upstream' mentality of the local, the peasant, the river enthusiast. Societies have built dams, canals, flood walls, bridges and other structures to stabilize river systems without, it seems, questioning the cause of the instability. Rather like medicine, we have used the equivalent of drugs and pain-killers to cure symptoms, whereas some claim 'the true human talent lies with holism and the longer term' (Newson, 1997).

Who are the 'actors' mentioned in this account and which 'sectors do they represent?

### Answer

The 'actors' are the farmer, foresters, hydrologist and civil engineers and the 'sectors' they represent are, respectively, farming, forestry, local government and engineering.

A problem may be perceived differently by people operating in different sectors. Sectoral approaches, as shown in Activity 2.1, have not proved to be effective at dealing with water-related environmental issues. Neither do they allow for the effective participation of all stakeholders. Although attitudes are changing, and *integrated* water management is now being recognized as the way to implement sustainability in the context of water issues, various stakeholders and institutions are still very much divided into different sectors and isolated from each other. The next section examines some of the main institutions involved in the water industry in England and Wales.

## The water industry and its institutions in England and Wales

Institutions have been defined by Priscoli as 'the embodiment of values in regularized patterns of behaviour'. In the context of water issues he says that:

> … water institutions and organizations supply and distribute water resources and reflect society's values towards equity, freedom and justice.

> (Priscoli, 1989)

As we will see, some water institutions will need reforms if equity, freedom and justice are to be better reflected through the sharing and use of water resources. In addition to the term 'water institutions', another term you will often encounter is 'water industry'. In Britain, it includes a variety of water actors, but mainly:

- the water companies (specialized in distributing and treating the resource);
- the water regulators (e.g. the Drinking Water Inspectorate, the Environment Agency and the Office of Water Services, OFWAT), which monitor quality and set the price regime that companies follow.

In England and Wales, 10 private water companies were created in 1988 and they became the owners of the entire water system. They supply water and sewerage services and charges are levied by them. Activity 2.2 examines the advantages and disadvantages of such privatization measures.

### Activity 2.2   Britain's private water companies — the 'great experiment'

For a long time in Britain, water was managed mainly by ten state-run water boards — the River Water Authorities (RWAs). The Water Act of 1989 separated out the utility (water supply and sewerage services) and resource regulation functions of these institutions, therefore ending the classic conflict between service provider and regulator. Prior to this Act, the RWAs had suffered from under-investment since the 1970s. There were two major problems:

- raising the capital for maintenance and improvement of the ageing (often 19th century) supply and sewerage infrastructure;
- meeting the increasingly stringent demands of EU directives on water quality.

Because EU rules do not permit private companies to self-regulate, the regulatory agencies had to remain in public ownership. Following the 1989 Water Act, the government sold its ten water boards to private corporations. Although emotions run high about profits being made out of this most fundamental of human needs, the water companies have had to spend huge sums on repairs and improvements throughout the UK. As upgrading costs continue to rise, European law has also imposed new wastewater regulations upon water companies, resulting in further expenditure. These improvements have had a positive impact on the environment, but the costs are in turn being passed from the shareholders to the disgruntled customers.

In the first decade of water privatization in the UK, there were many problems, such as tough penalties levied against customers who had not paid their bills. In 1991, in the early years of privatization, some 21 000 homes were disconnected from their water supply for such non-payment. Many viewed such stringent measures as ruthless, however, and there is now legislation to protect customers. In the UK a government watchdog organization (OFWAT) influences the price of water in order to ensure an appropriate balance between the cost to water companies for repairs, maintenance and upgrading, and the costs to consumers. Furthermore, as the government no longer provides the sewerage service, its regulatory agencies are able to police this area more effectively as well. There have been over 200 successful prosecutions of water companies in recent years and encouragingly, most water companies are now reducing water bills to customers. In addition, the Drinking Water Inspectorate (DWI) ensures that companies supply their customers with high quality water. Safe water and a cleaner environment come at a price; but whether that price should be paid directly to governments in the form of taxes, or to private corporations who profit from providing such a service, is still being debated, not only in the UK but all over the world.

List the pros and cons of water privatization in Britain.

### Answer

Pros:
- Service providers and the regulators are now separate entities. The independent regulators, retained within government are, as a consequence, able to regulate more effectively.
- Capital has been raised for the maintenance and improvement of the ageing supply and sewerage infrastructures and for meeting EU regulations.
- There have been environmental improvements.
- Legislation now protects the customers.
- The DWI ensures that water companies supply their customers with high quality water.

Cons:
- Profits are being made out of the most basic need for water and sanitation.
- Costs are passed to the customers.
- Homes are disconnected from the water supply for non-payment.

---

The advantages derived from the privatization of water companies in the UK seem to be greater than the disadvantages and the situation is improving. But doubts and scepticism about the 'marketization' of water are still very much alive and many cases have demonstrated that there is still room for further improvement. For example, the drought of 1995 exposed some of the privatized companies' weaknesses in maintaining a service. The situation was made worse than it would have been prior to privatization because the companies had chosen to under-invest in the infrastructure in order to pay higher dividends to their shareholders. This public exposure of company greed and culpability also meant that consumers were less willing to make sacrifices to conserve water, when the companies had clearly made no sacrifice at all. Water shortages were probably made more acute as a result.

This begs some important questions (often asked in the context of privatization) such as: do 'specialized' water institutions meet people's needs, and if they don't, shouldn't they be more open to consultation and participation? One could argue that it is in order to complement (and compensate) what private water companies can (or cannot) provide, that other (less specialized) institutions and actors also deal with water. Thus, in the UK these include government departments and agencies such as DETR (Department of the Environment, Transport and the Regions) and DEFRA (Department for the Environment, Food and Rural Affairs), the Environment Agency, English Nature, the Joint Nature Conservation Committee and, of course, land owners. The recognition of all of these as useful contributors to the understanding of water issues and to the improvement of critical situations is not straightforward. But the tendency to question who the water experts really are is certainly noticeable at the beginning of the 21st century. The answer to 'Who is in charge of water matters?' has changed with time. The ecological protection of aquatic systems in particular is now given much more importance, but further integration with general water policies is still required.

Currently, a range of stakeholders tends to be consulted in the decision-making process concerning water issues, but the market approach in the area of water management is also continuing to grow. Thus, the ten British water and sewerage companies (originally protected from takeover for five years by the British Government's 'golden share') were affected by the extension of major water markets. The smallest UK water companies are now all owned by multinational companies, mainly the French groups Vivendi, SAUR and Suez-Lyonnaise. These mergers (takeovers) show that the provision of services related to water has progressively become dominated by global water markets, in parallel with the globalization of participatory processes. These are the two main themes we will be focusing on in the next chapter.

## 2.6 Conclusion

In this chapter, we reviewed the vulnerability that humans and ecosystems face with regard to water. Our lives depend on water, but also on services provided by ecosystems that are themselves dependent on water. The intricate inter-relationships of all water needs and dependencies highlight the fact that, if we want to protect water (both quantity and quality), we first need to protect aquatic ecosystems.

We can conclude that water problems are due not only to water shortages, floods and water pollution, but are also directly caused by the way in which we manage the resource. We must learn to respect the inter-dependencies between ecosystems and human systems and reform our approaches to water management so that they are more ecologically sound and water is attainable by all. We need to learn not only how to respect these inter-dependencies, but also to reflect this understanding through innovative new water management systems. Currently, the water engineering, market-orientated, non-participatory approaches we tend to favour are not systemic nor ecologically appropriate.

The various issues that we examined in this chapter can be represented in a type of systems diagram called a systems map. One of the main objectives of a systems map is to focus on system boundaries and overlaps between them, as shown in Figure 2.12.

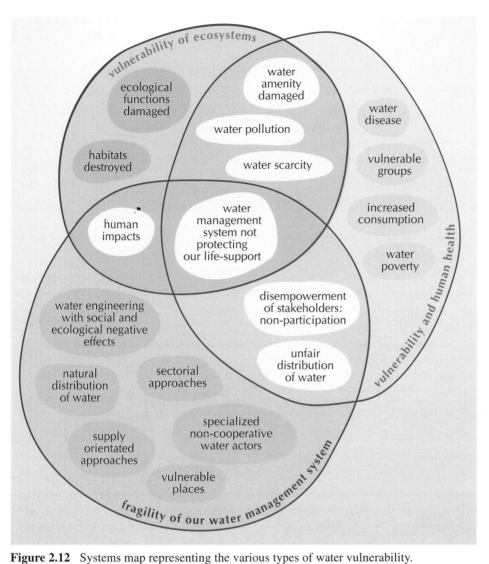

**Figure 2.12** Systems map representing the various types of water vulnerability.

You should go to the Web and complete the remaining activities for Chapter 2.

## 2.7 Summary of Chapter 2

In this chapter, we focused on the various dimensions of 'vulnerability' related to water issues. We saw that:

2.1    Water problems are experienced by millions of people in their daily life, around the world, especially in developing countries.

2.2 There are various types of vulnerability related to water issues: human health vulnerability, water shortages or floods, ecological vulnerability, fragility of our approaches and understanding of water issues, and unequal distribution of the resource.

2.3 Water is geographically, as well as economically and politically, unequally distributed in the world. Vulnerable groups include primarily poor populations.

2.4 Aquatic ecosystems perform four types of ecological functions (production, sink, life support, health). These are all interrelated. Threatening one ecological function generates a threat to the other ecological functions.

2.5 Ecosystems can be affected by natural disasters as well as by human activities.

2.6 There are different types of water pollution and water pollutants.

2.7 We are increasing our water vulnerability by adopting water management approaches that do not respect ecosystem functioning. Water engineering has been considered as an efficient technological fix for a long time. However, its negative ecological and social effects are now being highlighted.

2.8 A partial, sectoral understanding of water issues leads to partial, sectoral water responses. These non-holistic responses can in turn generate new problems.

2.9 We would benefit from having more varied water actors in the water sector than water companies versus regulators.

## Learning Outcomes for Chapter 2

When you have completed this chapter, you should be able to:

2.1 Define and use, or recognize definitions and applications of, each of the terms given in **bold** in the text. (Question 2.1)

2.2 Outline the reasons why humans are vulnerable to water problems. (Questions 2.2, 2.3 and 2.4)

2.3 Explain why the vulnerability of humans to water problems is very much related to the way in which the functioning of ecosystems can be damaged. (Questions 2.5, 2.6 and 2.7)

2.4 Explain why the way in which we manage water can constitute a type of (water) problem in itself. (Questions 2.8, 2.9, 2.10 and 2.11)

## Questions for Chapter 2

### Question 2.1

Define the following terms: ecosystem functioning; point and non-point sources of water pollution; eutrophication; acidification; water engineering.

## Question 2.2

In which ways are humans vulnerable to the *quantity* of water that is available to them? Answer this question by addressing each of the following: water shortages, floods, problems of allocation and natural distribution of the resource.

## Question 2.3

In which ways are humans vulnerable to the *quality* of water? In order to answer this question, concentrate on the effects that polluted water and aquatic ecosystems have on the lives of humans.

## Question 2.4

What is the current estimate of water-related deaths per year? What are the different types of water-related diseases?

## Question 2.5

Explain why each of the four services provided by aquatic ecosystems is crucial to the lives and welfare of humans.

## Question 2.6

Give some examples of threats to freshwater ecosystem functions that arise from human activities.

## Question 2.7

Explain why damaging one ecosystem function can affect the other ecosystem functions negatively.

## Question 2.8

Describe the stakeholders involved in the 'water sector' in the UK.

## Question 2.9

What is the role of UK water companies in 'water management'? What are the controversies associated with the privatization of water services?

## Question 2.10

Explain the advantages and shortcomings of using water engineering to meet water needs.

## Question 2.11

Why are 'sectoral approaches' to water management problematic, and how can this be remedied?

# References

Daily, G. C. (1997) *Nature's services. Societal dependence on natural ecosystems.* Washington: Island Press.

DeGroot, R. (1992) *Functions of Nature. Evaluation of nature in environmental planning, management and decision-makin*g. The Netherlands: Wolters-Noordhoff.

Freedman, B. (1989) *Environmental ecology. The impacts of pollution and other stresses on ecosystem structure and function.* London: Academic Press.

IUCN (2000) *Vision for Water and Nature. A World Strategy for Conservation and Sustainable Management of Water Resources in the 21st century.* Switzerland and Cambridge: IUCN, Gland, p. 44.

Miller, T. G. Jr (1998) (10th edn) *Living in the Environment. Principles, Connections and Solutions.* Belmont, CA: Wadsworth, p. 516.

Priscoli (1989) quoted in Newson, M. (1997) (2nd edn) *Land, water and development. Sustainable management of river basin systems.* London: Routledge.

World Resources Institute (2000) *World Resources 2000–2001. People and Ecosystems — The Fraying Web of Life.* Washington D.C: World Resources Institute.

UNEP (2002) *Global Environmental Outlook 3. Past, present and future perspectives.* London: Earthscan.

World Health Organization (1993) (2nd edn) *Guidelines for drinking water quality.* Geneva: WHO.

# Chapter 3  Water in a globalized world

**Prepared for the course team by Sandrine Simon**

## 3.1 Introduction

The hydrological cycle is a natural global phenomenon, but this is not the only reason why water has become a global environmental issue. Factors including trans-boundary pollution, international conflicts over shared water resources, inequalities of access, the involvement of the UN and the ownership of water resources by multinational companies, have all added extra dimensions to this globalization of water issues. Other important global environmental issues, such as climate change, also have a water dimension. Consequently, the slogan adopted by Agenda 21 to 'think globally, act locally', may not in practice be sufficient to address many of the environmental issues that involve water. With global resources such as water, it may in fact be better to start acting globally now, whilst simultaneously investigating ways in which local and large-scale actions can complement each other. In addition, since the various dimensions of water issues include ecological, socio-economic and political considerations, we also need to look beyond the economic sphere.

In this chapter, we are going to investigate three different aspects of the globalization of water issues:

- global water markets and their environmental consequences;
- international law relating to water and how it can contribute to the protection of both the natural resource and human users;
- global networks and new forms of institution that can help re-define globalization in the context of water management.

## 3.2 Global water markets

The economics of **global water markets** constitute an interesting example of globalization. One aim of water markets is to encourage a more efficient use of existing water supplies. Markets also allow users to sell their water rights (the right to have access to water and use it) to other consumers. In Chapter 2 we looked at the local water market that was created by the privatization of the UK water companies, a policy decision that was taken in an attempt to remove the huge cost of modernizing the infrastructure for water supply and sanitation from the UK Government's budget. With increasing globalization, water companies are trading in the international arena. For example, in 1999 a Franco–Spanish water company was selected by the Chilean Government to manage the water supply and sewerage for 44 districts of the capital city, Santiago (Figure 3.1). There was consensus that something had to be done to improve water services in the city. However, the ways to proceed and, in particular the seemingly opaque way in which future water prices were calculated, made people fear that not all groups of the population would benefit from the new 'improved services'. The question of how to supply *the poor* with water under a private multinational system is a source of heated public debate. As water becomes an international business, questions of who will monitor *fair* pricing practices on an international scale remain largely unanswered. While the Chilean government could allocate funds across various sectors linked to water when the industry was still in public ownership (through subsidies), this is a less effective measure, or impossible, when multinationals control the water supply.

**Figure 3.1** The use of a private multinational company to manage water in Santiago, Chile, is one example amongst many in Latin America.

So, does privatization of the water industry meet its objectives once a private company controls the water supply in a city? Box 3.1 illustrates such a scenario in another Latin American country, this time Bolivia.

## Box 3.1  Water privatization in La Paz (Bolivia): Lyonnaise des Eaux dominates the scene.

Alto Lima is the oldest and the poorest quarter of La Paz. In February 2002, the rain generates muddy streams that overflow from drains and spread over the streets which are not paved and are covered with domestic waste since there is no public cleaning. These streets are also unlit since this service has also been privatized. The nearest health centre is managed by a non-governmental organization (NGO). Antonio has lived in Alto Lima since his childhood. This popular quarter is located 4000 metres above sea-level; the richest city residents live at a lower altitude, 3200 metres above sea-level. It takes Antonio more than an hour to reach the centre of the town; too far and too expensive to go there using public transport. Antonio is unhappy because water, which flows abundantly here, is no longer available for his consumption. Since its distribution has been managed by the water company Lyonnaise des Eaux, its price has increased considerably. Most of the people in this quarter are unable to afford this price and now have to use communal 'bathrooms' — but even these are not free!

The privatization of water was followed by a deterioration of water services, and this can be linked to the large number of redundancies made by the company to reduce costs after takeover. For example, the team of 18 technicians who controlled nearly 80 000 water meters each month, was reduced by half and the reduced team was then allocated to other maintenance tasks instead! As a result, the water consumption of each household is rarely checked, so that whatever the water flow, the same bill is levied. Paradoxically, Lyonnaise des Eaux had based its campaign on the fact that it could and would improve water services and extend the water network. But the reality is quite different. Breakdowns are more frequent because maintenance is less frequent and so it takes longer to repair the infrastructure (pipes etc.), to restore supply or to stop wastage arising from leaks. People have even resorted to re-using old wells to ensure that their businesses can survive.

During the last 5 years, the salary of the directors has increased from 12 000 to 65 000 B (Bolivianos) per month. At the same time, the cost of a domestic water supply has risen to 1100 B per annum, against less than 730 B over 5 years before privatization, even though the average wage of workers has only reached 1800 B. 'Nowadays, it is a luxury to have water in Alto Lima', notes a former worker from Lyonnaise des Eaux, who has not been able to afford a water supply since he was made redundant.

'The objective was to demonstrate that Lyonnaise des Eaux can deal with difficult areas', explains the director of the Bolivian branch of Lyonnaise des Eaux. But the results are not convincing. As a maintenance worker says, 'they promised us new equipment, they only painted pipes in white'. In other countries, some privatized companies have been condemned for failing to meet minimal hygiene standards. But here in La Paz (in February 2002), Lyonnaise des Eaux has only been condemned for cutting water to municipal centres (including all the schools in town) for several weeks. Despite this condemnation however, water cuts are still made with impunity and without warning, and some parts of Alto Lima are permanently deprived of a safe water supply.

Why do the inhabitants of these quarters accept — with the seemingly indifferent and optimistic patience that external observers often project onto the most impoverished people — such a lack of consideration? Perhaps they feel under-valued by the rest of society and do not have a recognized platform where they can express their needs and demands for future action. So despite talks of improving partnerships between different stakeholders in society (see, for instance, the outcomes of the World Summit on Sustainable Development in Johannesburg, 2003), the gap carries on widening between political elites and the rest of the population.

(summarized and adapted from Franck Poupeau, le Monde Diplomatique, 2002)

○ List the various issues that are causing problems as a consequence of the Lyonnaise Des Eaux management of water affairs in La Paz.

○

- Deterioration of living conditions.
- Although water is abundant, it is not available for poor people's consumption.
- Water prices have increased greatly since *Lyonnaise des Eaux* took control.
- Deterioration of water services.
- Redundancies in the water service industry.
- Poor maintenance of the infrastructure.

- People use old wells (and potentially polluted water) as a substitute for a safe domestic water supply.

- Water workers and users are generally worse off.

- Water cuts are experienced on a regular basis.

- Lack of institutional and political support for the users.

The Bolivian example is not an isolated case. Global water markets are dominated by two big French multinational companies: Vivendi (formerly Generale des Eaux) and Suez (formerly Lyonnaise des Eaux). Together, they have captured more than 40% of the global water market. Some people estimate the potential of this global water market to be very substantial, which may explain the labelling of water as 'blue gold' — though *better* than gold' seems a more appropriate description since measuring the value of water through a pricing system is problematic. Water is priceless, it is life!

So, should water be free at the point of use? The 'problem' here is that, when water is not valued, users waste it and people don't use water conservation technologies. There is not enough investment to maintain water infrastructure and research and training systems and, as a result, the sector becomes conservative and stagnant. If we need to find ways of valuing water, we must do this through a fair system of pricing for those in the developed world who can afford to pay, alongside conservation measures and a fair system of allocation and management of the resource. Do global water markets achieve this and do they use water efficiently?

The development of efficient water markets depends on a number of conditions, including the ability of the seller to establish *ownership* over the resource. In addition, for markets to operate in the public interest, the interests of third parties (including environmental interests and those of populations living downstream of any large transfer) must also be considered. As we will see later, this last point has triggered many controversies. The assumption that markets take third parties into consideration is currently as unrealistic as asserting that water markets are apolitical, fair and ethical. This is not a cynical remark and, to appreciate this point, we need to understand where water management sits in the context of other markets.

Policies such as the ones generated by the World Bank (WB), the International Monetary Fund (IMF) and the General Agreement on Tariffs and Trade (GATT), are based on the premise that the future growth of developing countries depends upon their ability to export primary products to rich nations. But producing cash crops for export, rather than subsistence crops, has created all sorts of water problems, not least of which is an inequality in the distribution and allocation of water. One classic case is the production of cotton for export by many developing countries such as Ethiopia.

Cotton crops (Figure 3.2) are particularly 'thirsty'. Their production has caused environmental degradation and social and economic problems in many parts of the world. During Ethiopia's third Five-year Plan, 60% of the lands cultivated in the fertile Awash Valley were devoted to cotton production. As happened in Burkina Faso and Mali, the local pastoralists were evicted from their traditional pastures and pushed into the fragile uplands. Environmental degradation was accelerated by the clearance of wooded areas and the encroachment on land that was previously used for food crops. The result of this pressure on resources is a shortage of land for small-scale farmers and a breakdown of the traditional system of agriculture in which fields were allowed to rest. The tree clearance has also led to a shortage of wood for fuel in the villages.

Villagers have been forced to use cow dung and cotton stalks for fuel, instead of using these in the traditional manner to replenish soil fertility in areas already vulnerable to drought and erosion.

**Figure 3.2** The cultivation of cotton crops places a great demand on water.

This example is a good illustration of the types of impacts that some agricultural measures can have on environmental, social and water systems. To an extent, it also illustrates the fact that economic globalization principles, encompassed in the GATT, contradict what water markets are (at least in theory) trying to achieve — a better distribution of the natural resource.

The ways in which various countries and stakeholders of the world can use water for these developments will have to be critically tackled, sooner or later. Consequently the angle taken on the water crisis at the WSSD, for instance (water targets focused mainly on the need to improve sanitation) may indeed have resulted in the failure to address the very problem of access to water for all. In effect, limiting ourselves to installing new water infrastructures will not be enough to ensure the fair allocation of water in different places in the world.

As Ward says:

> Old-fashioned imperialism is dead, but has been replaced by a far more efficient economic imperialism, which obliges the poor world to destroy its precarious economy and environment, to benefit the consumer economy of the rich world. Water which could be managed to provide a local livelihood is squandered for the sake of a highly competitive export market or for the tourist industry. The casualties of the global market are the local populations, deprived of a water supply.

(Ward, 1997)

And this goes even beyond the GATT: the globalization of 'luxury tourism' is also quietly contradicting what water markets are, in theory, aspiring to. As Croall explains:

> Thousands of peasant families have been turned off their land to make way for the increasing number of golf courses being built in Southeast Asia to cater for tourists and others [see Figure 3.3]. As a result, Amnesty International has had to create a new category of 'golfing' prisoners of conscience. In Thailand, between 1989 and 1994, local developers created 160 courses, most of them out of rice fields in agricultural regions. Though the golf courses are supposed to be self sufficient, it is claimed that they take water from reservoirs illegally, or dam up streams that flow through them towards the reservoir, so making drought conditions worse.

(Croall, 1995)

**Figure 3.3** A green golf course in the Egyptian desert — water for a very few.

The liberalization of international trade has affected the water market and the profits made by multinational water companies are a direct result of the de-regulation of global trade, with the approval of international institutions and national governments. The meeting of the WTO in Qatar in 2001 further encouraged the privatization. Under the title 'Trade and Environment', Article 31(iii) requires the 'reduction or elimination of tariff and non-tariff barriers to environmental goods' — and, surprisingly, these include water! Any attempt to control the (commercial) 'export' of water has therefore been made illegal, and Article 32 actually prohibits governments from imposing non-tariff barriers — such as laws that protect their own environment!

So is there no hope; does the commodification and economic valuation of water have to embrace the vicious circles of environmental degradation and social inequalities that unfettered economic globalization can generate? Despite this grim state of affairs, many people are now advancing an economic case for social justice in access to water and sanitation. The provision of public standpipes to provide cheap (or even free) water to low income groups could increase economic efficiency while improving the position of the poor and hence achieving greater equity. It would reduce both the time spent collecting water as well as the adverse health effects arising from the consumption of polluted water. Of course, there is also a political and ethical case for making access to safe water more equitable. If the international community is keen to prevent environmental degradation, conserve water and maintain its quality, the policies it formulates will have to take account of economic and political considerations.

The problem is that new equitable principles in water markets have not yet reached the sphere of multinational water companies. At an international level, the water targets agreed at the World Summit on Sustainable Development, still focus mainly on access to water and sanitation and do not address the deep economic problems that underlie the crisis of '**food insecurity**' throughout the world. So far, it has been left to NGOs like Oxfam to insist that the elementary principle of using water for human needs is that of '*some for all rather than all for some*':

> Many of the innovative projects that reached low income groups with improved housing and basic services come from NGOs or municipal authorities in the South, many implemented with no support from aid agencies … The enormous failure to provide water, sanitation and health care and the huge health burden these impose on urban populations, seem unmanageable when aggregated. But if these problems in each city and municipality can be addressed by more competent and accountable local authorities working with citizens' groups, NGOs and other local participants, the problem appears more manageable.

(Satterthwaite, 1995)

From a political and social perspective, this raises serious concerns about systems of water governance and also about social and political stability. In 1997, a group of people in Tucuman (Argentina) started a movement of 'civil disobedience' against the water company Vivendi, by refusing to pay their water bills because of the deterioration in water quality and the doubling of water charges. In Bolivia, the people of Cochabamba formed a coalition in defence of water and life and they have been described by some as 'water warriors'. Though these protests were non-violent, this may not be the case for similar ones in the future.

On CD-ROM 4, you will find more examples of responses to water globalization and privatization, which you may want to read about when you have finished this chapter.

Is there any chance that global institutions might assist in the implementation of a more equal system of water charging and allocation? New debates on water rights, the principles of ecosystem protection (highlighted in various international water agreements), and new notions of participation and governance promise improvement in this sphere. They all stress the fact that it is time we managed water resources differently. We will return to these issues and potential 'solutions' in the next chapter. For the moment we will examine international law in the following section.

## 3.3 The internationalization of water laws

So far we have concentrated on one aspect of water and globalization: global water markets. But globalization is not always about the global economy. It can also be about the globalization of the legal system. Since so many environmental issues are long-term and can affect large geographical areas, the formulation of a solid international environmental legal system is crucial. Here, we will look at what is happening in the area of international water law.

Understanding what water laws are trying to achieve can be helped by distinguishing between the ownership of water and the right to have both access to water and use of it. The right to use water is based either on **customary** or **statutory** claims, which must be clearly identified before any regulation is possible. Customary rights may include the right to expropriate, use or trade water: these are the types of rights on which systems of community ownership or use and water charges can be built. However, systems based only on customary rights may not be able to ensure an efficient and equitable allocation of a scarce resource. A 'water legal system' not only needs mechanisms of ensuring access to water rights, but also a system of obligations regarding the usage and control of the levying of water charges by individuals. Statutory rights are those that are recognised and or authorized by statute.

Laws and regulations provide the framework within which water policies are put into effect. Among their key purposes are the protection of public health, the protection of natural resources and the prevention of unfair pricing. Legal instruments provide the mechanism for translating policy into practical implementation. They can facilitate cross-sectoral actions and provide mechanisms for dealing with conflict resolution. The formulation of such water legislation should include water ownership, rights of usage and authority to regulate.

Water laws exist at the national, regional, and international levels and a real consistency between these different scales must be found. International law is vital because of the water disputes that can arise over shared rivers for instance, or because of trans-boundary pollution. Such disputes might be unsolvable without the help of strong, enforceable, international water laws.

On a large scale, weak water policies, or water conflicts between various countries, have shown that the formulation and implementation of water law is not an easy matter. But progress is being made. Thus, some umbrella institutions have been created in an attempt to prevent water disputes. For example, the TECCONILE committee was set up to assist participating countries in the development, conservation and use of the Nile Basin water reserves in an integrated and sustainable manner (Calder, 1999).

Another example here dates from 1997, when the UN General Assembly adopted a convention on '*Non-navigable uses of international watercourses*', and invited member states and regional economic integration organizations to become parties. The aim here was to guide nations in the negotiation of agreements on specific watercourses. It is the most recent body of international legislation for negotiation and conflict resolution concerning trans-boundary waters, and brings the hope that a more harmonized and appropriate legal system can be created, accompanied by the creation of integrated global water institutions.

The extension of water law from the national to the international level is also taking place, though at a slow pace despite the urgent need. There is a move towards treating water issues in a broader and more systemic way. The internationalization of water law as an institution is, however, a very different process from that happening in water markets. While the globalization of water markets embraces the existing economic and political paradigm (under which the generation of profit and the preservation of power structures seem to prevail, unfortunately), the internationalization of water laws attempts to ensure (often with great difficulty) first and foremost that principles of equity, in particular, are protected. One example of a more comprehensive water legal system is that of the **European Water Framework Directive** (Box 3.2 and Figure 3.4).

## Box 3.2. The European Water Framework Directive (WFD)

| Key facts: the water situation in the EU | The Water Framework Directive (WFD) |
|---|---|

**Key facts: the water situation in the EU**

- 20% of all surface water in the EU is seriously threatened with pollution.

- Groundwater supplies around 65% of all Europe's drinking water.

- 60% of European cities over-exploit their groundwater resources.

- 50% of wetlands have 'endangered status' due to groundwater over-exploitation.

- The area of irrigated land in Southern Europe has increased by 20% since 1985.

**Figure 3.4** The EU Water Framework Directive is one of the official initiatives that is attempting to improve our water management practices.

**The Water Framework Directive (WFD)**

The WFD expands the scope of water protection to all waters and sets clear objectives that a 'good status' must be achieved for all European waters by 2015 and that water use must be sustainable throughout Europe.

The new over-arching WFD represents an innovative approach to water management. Key elements of the legislation include:

- The protection of all waters; rivers, lakes, coastal waters and groundwaters.

- The setting of ambitious objectives to ensure that all waters meet 'good' quality standards by 2015.

- The requirement for cross border co-operation between countries and all involved parties.

- Ensuring the active participation of all stakeholders including NGOs and local communities, in water management activities.

- Requiring water pricing policies and ensuring that the polluter pays — the WFD does *not* require *one* set price for water across the European Union (prices will vary depending on factors such as the internalization of environmental costs). But it requires the *transparency* underpinning water charging decisions across Europe.

- Balancing the interests of the environment with those who depend on it.

### Milestones of the Water Framework Directive:

| 2003 | 2004 | 2006 | 2008 | 2009 | 2015 |
|---|---|---|---|---|---|
| National and regional water laws to be adapted to the WFD. River basin co-operation to be made operational. | Analysis of pressures and impacts on our waters, as well as economic analysis, completed. | Monitoring programmes have to be operational as a basis for water management. | River Basin Management plans presented to the public. | Publishing first River Basin Management plans. | Water to meet 'good' quality standards. |

(Source: European Commission (2002) The Water Framework Directive: DG Environment, Luxembourg.)

The Water Framework Directive (WFD) of the European Union (EU), defines the conditions for common approaches, principles and political agreements that will be the basis of future action in Europe. Its first target is for national and regional laws to be adapted to the more global perspective of the WFD. The latter is an important example of the internationalization of water law, even though it only applies within EU boundaries. In the broader geographical sphere there is a small, but growing number of multilateral agreements, mainly concerned with specific watercourses or drainage basins. Although none of these agreements contain general principles that are immediately applicable to international law, there are three institutions which are focusing their research on this area. These institutions are: The Institut de Droit International (Institute of International Law), the International Law Association (ILA) and the International Law Commission (ILC) of the UN. As Ohlsson explains:

> The most general principle emerging from this work seems to be the one of *equitable use* (determined in each specific case) *and benefit* of a specific watercourse. The commentaries to the Helsinki Rules (formulated by ILA in 1966) make it explicitly clear that an existing use of a river would have to give way to a new use in order to reach an equitable apportioning, although the new user would have to pay compensation. ILC, on the other hand, which is bound by directives from the UN General Assembly, stresses the principle of not inflicting harm on present users (building on principles from the 1972 UN Conference on Human Environment and Development), thus unfortunately leaving equitable use out of the picture: the latter approach would seem to encourage a 'race for the river', where the first user will possess all rights.
>
> (Ohlsson, 1995)

Legal reforms still have a long way to go if international water law is to reflect new systemic, integrative and participatory ways of thinking in water management. In particular, the formulation and implementation of new international water laws will require new platforms or institutions that are based on consultation and participation. Existing institutions generally keep specialized 'water actors' apart from each other and thus do not fulfil the necessary criteria for fresh progress. Consequently, it is argued that a new concept of umbrella water institutions is needed and that such initiatives can be catalysed by global networks. This challenge is examined in the following section.

## 3.4 Global water networks

The creation of new, more integrated platforms or institutions — **water networks** is taking place at both a local and an international level. The UN has addressed this need, even though it has also been slow to react to water issues. Basic research on water issues was initiated by UNESCO in the 1960s and this ultimately led to the first UN World Water Conference, which took place in 1977 in Mar del Plata, Argentina (Figure 1.2). However, except for the Water Decade of 1981–1990, and attention given to the problems with international rivers, work on water issues in the wider sense has not been embraced fully by the UN. More recently, the 2002 World Summit on Sustainable Development (WSSD) pursued efforts initiated throughout the various World Water Forums (WWF). This summit had a strong emphasis on partnerships and water networks between various stakeholders (Figure 3.5).

**W**ater = We should be able to help at least one billion people without drinking water and two billion without sanitation.

**E**nergy = Electricity and other modern energy services should reach the more than two billion without them, while reducing over-consumption, promoting renewable energy and addressing climate change through a ratified Kyoto Protocol.

**H**ealth = Halt the deaths of three million people each year from air pollution, addressing effects of toxic and hazardous materials, and lower the incidence of malaria and African guinea worm — spread through polluted water and poor sanitation.

**A**griculture = Assure protection to two-thirds of the world's agricultural lands affected by land degradation by reversing it.

**B**iodiversity = Build 'a new ethic of global stewardship', challenging processes that have destroyed about half of the world's tropical rainforest and mangroves, threatened more than two-thirds of the world's coral reefs and decimated the planet's fisheries.

**Figure 3.5** Water was one of the five main themes addressed at the World Summit on Sustainable Development (Johannesburg, 2003).

In common with local initiatives, new international initiatives are based on the value of participation in water management and we will focus on such participation in Chapter 4. At an international level, the difference is that the use of the World Wide Web (WWW) is helping various types of stakeholder from around the world to communicate with each other. One important advantage of the WWW is that it bypasses institutional constraints that might prevent the participation of certain groups of stakeholders. In this way, the WWW can give disadvantaged groups a voice. But this can only happen if they are helped to gain access to the WWW in the first place, together with appropriate training. The possibilities for sharing knowledge and best practices on water management throughout the world are then very promising.

Problems of access to information and the Web have been addressed by one particular project, called the 'Access Initiative'. This initiative' collects information on water quality to ensure general water safety and ensures that people are more aware of where the pollution is, and what the dangers are, through a rigorous water quality monitoring system. The Access Initiative seeks to introduce consistent standards to track public access to information, participation and justice related to the water environment. It has engaged in research to measure and improve access to the WWW around the world. It has highlighted the fact that, while the Internet can be a powerful tool to disseminate information, access to the Internet is not widespread enough to reach the majority of the world's people. New efforts are needed to overcome the scarcity of information about water quality and safety. To this end, the Access Initiative recommends that national governments should:

- integrate water quality monitoring systems and share information across agencies;
- design and implement standard procedures for responding to data requests made by individuals, the media and citizens' groups;
- actively disseminate information.

**Figure 3.6** Logo Streams of Knowledge.

There are other global networks however, that do not seem to rely on the Web. One of these is the 'Streams of Knowledge', a coalition of nine organizations that are keen to work together to improve water and sanitation by sharing knowledge about individual and joint experiences from the past (Figure 3.6). The coalition activities that are adding value to individual activities include:

- help in strengthening other resource centres;
- developing regional activities, networks and alliances;
- raising funds to facilitate access to Streams of Knowledge information and other services.

There are also numerous Web-based initiatives that have been developed with the aim of consolidating global water networks. A few are:

- Fourth Water Information Summit, 2001: 'Internet based mechanisms and partnerships to build virtual capacity for sustainable water resource management'. This meeting confirmed the practicality of using the Web as a tool in the sector of water management.
- The Water Environment Federation (WEF) and the International Water Academy for example, have taken responsibility for making their 'water vision' a reality.

A Virtual Water Forum (Figure 3.7) was organized in the context of the Third Water Forum and this went online in June 2001.

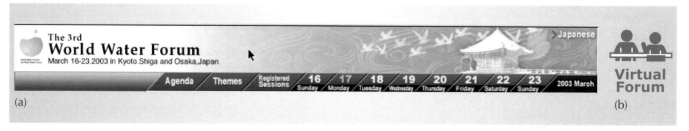

**Figure 3.7** A Virtual Forum (b), was used to prepare the 3rd World Water Forum (a), through a consultation process.

The Virtual Water Forum tried to:

- provide a venue for continuing discussion;
- act as a facilitator to open discussions;
- maximize participation in discussion.

Thus, the use of Web portals (for example Figure 3.8) can help in questioning our current governance of water issues by somehow democratizing the debate and decision-making process. Three examples of e-democracy via dialogues on water issues are described in Box 3.3.

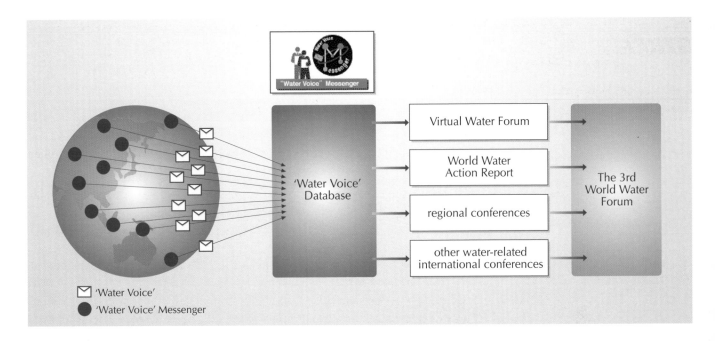

**Figure 3.8** The Virtual Water Forum is part of a broader 'Water Voice Messenger project', which enlarges the Web-consultation process even further.

## Box 3.3 Examples of global networks established through 'Dialogues'

### Dialogue on Water, Food and the Environment

A 'Dialogue on Water, Food and the Environment' has been created to help bridge the chasm between agriculture and environmental communities over the way in which water should be managed — Figure 3.9. Its founding organizations range from UN agencies to associations of farmers, irrigation engineers, environmental organizations, water umbrella organizations and water research teams.

The goal of the dialogue is to provide a multi-stakeholder learning framework focused on 3 main themes:

- developing shared values related to food security and environmental sustainability at national and basin levels;

- a knowledge base of credible and authoritative information;

- local action activities that aim to provide an information exchange and best practice identification platform.

**Figure 3.9** The Dialogue on Water, Food and the Environment is another web platform where various shareholders can share their knowledge and views.

## *Dialogue on effective water governance*

Water governance refers to the range of political, socio-economic and administrative systems that are in place to regulate the development and management of water resources and provision of water services at different levels in society. The dialogue brings stakeholders together to examine political processes and governance systems and provides a platform for communication, negotiation, social learning and collective decision-making. It helps to build trust between concerned actors from the government, the market and civil society and works towards overcoming barriers to change.

Dialogue activities include political roundtables, assessment of government systems, reflections on lessons learned from previous practices and the identification of best practice. The dialogue is aimed at strengthening the Integrated Water Management toolbox that has been developed by the Global Water Partnership (GWP).

## *Dialogue on water and climate*

The World Meteorological Organization (WMO), the United Nations Educational Scientific and Cultural Organization (UNESCO), the world conservation union (IUCN) and many others, have initiated the multi-stakeholder dialogue on water and climate. This is a platform designed to bridge the information gaps between the water managers and the community of researchers on climate change, in order to improve the ability of water managers to cope with the impacts of increasing climate variability and change. The dialogue is organized to share information on coping strategies and actions between science and water managers and to raise awareness among policy makers and users, including the public. The activities include:

- initiating policy-orientated dialogues at national, regional and basin levels to improve coping capacities;

- facilitating and stimulating the development of analytical and training tools;

- raising awareness about the links between climate change and water.

Do you feel that these dialogues are open equally to all types of stakeholders?

Although these dialogues seem to be, in principle, very open processes, the types of networks they generate, therefore, seem to be very much focused on governmental and international institutions as well as water experts. Although the dialogue, at this level, extends beyond national boundaries and disciplinary perspectives, participation might remain relatively narrow in practice.

Observing the various types of 'Dialogues' above may imply that there is a need for better coordination and communication between networks at various geographical levels. The local knowledge on water practices in various parts of the world would benefit from being shared globally. Here again, an improvement in the inter-relations, inter-dependencies and links between local levels and global networks is becoming an imperative. We need to re-define what the 'globalization of water issues' means in terms of perspectives and responses.

# 3.5 Conclusion

In this chapter, we have examined three very different faces of 'globalization' in the context of water management:

- The first one focused on the globalization of water markets and the domination of multinational companies such as Vivendi and Suez around the world (and increasingly in developing countries).

- The second face of globalization focused on a second type of institution: that of water laws.

- Thirdly we examined a new type of platform that has the potential to by-pass the constraints of existing national or other international institutions: the global water networks, often hosted in a Web portal.

These various tendencies in water globalization are all derived from the fact that we need to develop a more systemic understanding of water issues, with new systems of water monitoring and governance. Figure 3.10 illustrates the progression towards a new type of water governance, as shown in this chapter. It is an 'influence diagram' — an appropriate use of systems diagrams since the creation of a new water governance is influenced by a variety of actors and factors.

One important concluding message is that, in order to meet the needs of both people and ecosystems, globalized approaches to water management must take account of the local situation (Figure 3.10).

Now go to the Web and complete the activities associated with this part of the chapter.

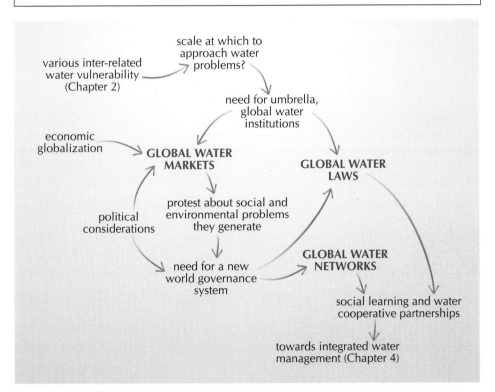

**Figure 3.10** The various faces of water globalized responses.

While certain forms of globalization (such as water markets) are, by their very nature, prone to ignore local needs, some others such as water laws and water networks make a virtue of doing so.

## 3.6 Summary of Chapter 3

3.1 The globalization of water is not only represented by the globalization of water markets. Global water networks and international water laws also exist and present another face of 'water globalization'.

3.2 The provision and treatment of water seems to be a lucrative business. However, users often seem to be the losers; water needs are often less well-met after a water multinational takes over water affairs.

3.3 The *willingness* to pay for water does not equate with the *ability* to pay for water.

3.4 The development of efficient water markets depends on a number of conditions, including the capability of the seller to establish ownership over the resource. In theory, for markets to operate in the public interest, the interests of third parties (environment and downstream populations) need to be considered. Frequently however, these are not respected.

3.5 The main objectives and tendencies of the international market economy seem to contradict the principles of fair allocation of water and the consideration of access to water as a human right.

3.6 Water laws and regulations provide the framework within which water policies are put into effect. Among their key purposes are the protection of public health, the protection of natural resources and the prevention of unfair pricing.

3.7 International water law is difficult to formulate and implement. However, texts such as the law of the non-navigable uses of international watercourses are slowly being formulated and these should help to resolve international water conflicts.

3.8 The creation of new, more integrated, *platforms* or *institutions* is taking place at a local level (as in Agenda 21 initiatives) but also at an international level.

3.9 Global Water Networks are a form of global participatory process that need to be connected to local knowledge and action, and that may rely on the use of the WWW. The WWW, as an alternative sort of platform, can help in giving a voice to people who cannot express their views or share knowledge in their countries' institutions.

3.10 There are positive and negative aspects to all forms of 'water globalization' — although some of them seem more appropriate in helping protect people and the environment.

## Learning Outcomes for Chapter 3

When you have completed this chapter, you should be able to:

3.1 Define and use, or recognize definitions and applications of, each of the terms given in **bold** in the text. (Question 3.1)

3.2 Describe and critically analyse the three faces of water globalization examined in this chapter. (Questions 3.2, 3.3 and 3.4)

3.3 List various types of global institutions, water laws and directives. (Questions 3.5 and 3.6)

3.4 Explain why the World Wide Web constitutes a promising platform that responds to the need for institutional reform. (Question 3.7)

## Questions for Chapter 3

### Question 3.1

What is the difference between the 'global dimensions' of water issues and 'water globalization'?

### Question 3.2

What are the pros and cons of global water markets?

### Question 3.3

What are the pros and cons of international water laws?

### Question 3.4

What are the pros and cons of global water networks?

### Question 3.5

Give the name of three main international institutions that are currently working on water international laws.

### Question 3.6

What is the European Water Framework Directive trying to achieve?

### Question 3.7

Provide some examples of global water networks on the Web. Explain what they can achieve that non-web platforms cannot.

# References

Croall (1995) *Preserve or destroy: tourism and the environment*. London: Calouste Gulbenkian Foundation, p. 46.

Earth Council (1994) *The Earth Summit. ECO 92. Different Visions.* San Jose, Costa Rica: IICA

European Commission (2002) *The Water Framework Directive*: *Tap into it!* Luxembourg: European Commission.

Green Cross International (2000) *National sovereignty and international watercourses.* Switzerland: Green Cross International.

Ohlsson L. (1995) *Hydropolitics. Conflicts over water as a development constraint.* London: Zed Publications.

Postel, S. (1996) *Dividing the waters: food security, ecosystem health, and the new politics of scarcity.* Washington: World Watch Institute.

Poupeau, F. (2002) '*Et l'eau de la Paz fut privatisee*'. Le Monde Diplomatique, 28 May 2002.

Satterthwaite (1995) *The underestimation of urban poverty and of its health consequence*: Third World Planning Review, **17**, No. 4.

Ward C. (1997) *Reflected in water. A crisis of social responsibility.* London: Cassell.

# Chapter 4 Towards sustainable water management

**Prepared for the course team by Sandrine Simon**

## 4.1 Introduction

In the previous chapters of this book, we focused on:

- the importance of water issues and responses in the 21st century;
- the varied types of vulnerability that generate the world water crisis;
- the various faces of water globalization.

We looked at a range of response to the water crisis and discussed how some could help improve the situation while others might generate further problems. At this stage we want to identify some viable solutions to the water crisis. To this end, we will examine the notions of sustainable and integrated water management and then examine the links between local and global actions in the context of a new governance system for water management.

By the end of this chapter, you should have a clearer idea about the most pressing water problems, and what type of actions should be prioritized if they are to help us implement **sustainable water management (SWM)**. We will examine what sustainability means in the context of water management, together with potential transitions to SWM. The chapter will conclude with a discussion about integrated water management (IWM), an approach that promises much in the context of integration and participation.

## 4.2 What does sustainability mean in the context of water management?

Sustainability is a complex concept, which has been the object of debate and controversy for decades. You have already examined some dimensions of this concept in previous blocks. Here we are just going to focus on what it means in the context of water management. From a *physical* perspective, the sustainability of water management implies a renewal of the resource (replenishment of water reserves). In addition, as we will see, managing water in a sustainable way has implications for ecosystems as well as for economic and social systems.

### 4.2.1 The sustainability of the water environment

When considering the sustainability of the water environment, the biophysical charactersitics are the easiest to describe. Thus, the key element in SWM must be the retention of sufficient water reserves within natural systems for a variety of reasons that include, for example, the protection of habitats and the dilution, biodegradation and removal of pollutants. SWM is therefore characterized by the protection of the ecological functions of water ecosystems. Focusing merely on the conservation of a certain quantity of water is not enough. What we need is a healthy aquatic environment which contributes to the cleaning of the water and therefore, in the process, also to the preservation of a healthy habitat for humans and all other species (Figure 4.1).

**Figure 4.1** Maintaining ecological integrity is crucial to the welfare of human societies since we depend on ecological services.

## 4.2.2 The economic sustainability of water management

Water is vital for economic activities. The question is, what does it mean to use it in a sustainable way? The answer is simple: economic dimensions of sustainable development shift the emphasis towards the efficient long-term use of water resources and are directly related to its social dimensions. Economic efficiency thus revolves around two elements:

- the allocation of available water resources between competing users and uses in a way that optimizes the total welfare derived from the resource.

- the development of least-cost supply schemes that ensure that the benefits from additional supply exceed the costs that this additional supply might generate (including the costs imposed on the environment).

Although these principles seem logical, implementing them is not always straightforward: comparing costs and benefits implies that these can easily be identified and measured but this is not always the case. Both the lack of methodological tools and the political will to develop or improve these tools, seem to contribute to slowing down the identification and implementation of SWM measures, hence reinforcing the belief that the water crisis is, to a large extent, a crisis in management (Figure 4.2).

**Saving water in industry**

– Make a corporate commitment to water efficiency
– Equipment changes: high efficiency, water saving equipment
– Operating and maintenance procedures (e.g. detection and repair of all leaks)
– Better landscape irrigation (e.g. use wastewater for irrigation)
– Save water used in industrial production processes

**Saving water in agriculture**

40% of the world depends on irrigation. But surface irrigation is highly inefficient: most of the water is lost through evaporation
Techniques such as drip irrigation can help in saving water
They combine
– the calculation of the amount of water the crop requires and
– the monitoring of the depletion of available water in the crop to root zone

**Saving water in cities**

– Metering of parks
– Low water use landscaping
– Development of recycling facilities to use treated wastewater rather than drinking water for irrigation and in the treatment process
– Toilets could be progressively replaced with low-flow fixtures

**Figure 4.2** The water crisis is mainly a crisis in management. Efficient, sustainable ways of managing the resource must be found.

## 4.2.3 The social dimensions of sustainable water management

Very closely related to the economic dimensions of water management are its social dimensions. Measures which ensure the long-term sustainability of the water environment should ensure that all consumers have enough water to satisfy their basic needs and maintain their livelihoods. Sustainable development defined in terms of equity, basic human needs and the protection of distinct communities might require different sets of management strategies to be implemented.

Here again, implementing measures that protect the social dimensions of SWM emerges from both a strong political will to address the water crisis, and the involvement of a variety of stakeholders (Figure 4.3). The link between the two can emerge, for instance, from dialogues. SWM involves the combination of the ecological, economic and social dimensions examined above and can be described as follows:

> An effective strategy for the sustainable management of water resources involves preserving the ecological integrity of water supply systems, wasting less water, allowing fair access to water supplies, and giving people a say in how water resources are developed and used (i.e. participatory decision-making).

> (Miller, 1998)

Miller's quote outlines the basic principles to follow when attempting to improve the management of water resources. In the next section, we examine how systems thinking can help us refine our understanding of SWM.

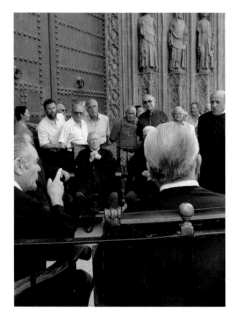  

**Figure 4.3** The participation of various stakeholders in water management will help in finding better management practices.

## 4.3 Transition to sustainability

We are now going to identify how the various dimensions of SWM are reflected in water policies. The **seven sustainability criteria** that Gleick (1995) has suggested, can help us to do this. The criteria correspond to the *objectives* that, in his opinion, any (water-related) policy aimed at SWM should meet. These criteria are listed below:

1   A minimum water requirement should be guaranteed to all humans to maintain health.

2   Sufficient water should be guaranteed to restore and maintain the health of ecosystems.

3   Data on water resource availability, use and quality should be collected and made accessible to all parties.

4   Water quality should be maintained to certain standards.

5   Human actions should not damage the long term renewability of freshwater stocks and flows.

6   Institutional mechanisms should be set up to prevent and resolve conflicts over water.

7   Water planning and decision-making should be democratic, ensuring representation of all affected parties and fostering direct participation of affected interests.

This set of criteria can be used to check whether water management policies are attempting to implement sustainability principles. One example of a new water policy in the UK is the **River Basin Management (RBM)** initiative. Table 4.1 shows the 'sustainable stages' (*strong* to *weak*) reached by this type of policy.

**Table 4.1** A possible map of sustainable transition (Source: modified from Pearce, 1993). (Note: italics indicate the stage reached in the UK with River Basin Management.)

| Degree of sustainability | Policy | Economy | Society | Contact |
|---|---|---|---|---|
| *Stage 1:* | lip service to | *minor tinkering with* | little awareness | discussion amongst businesses |
| ultra weak | integrated policies | *economic instruments* | /media coverage | consultation exercises |
| *Stage 2:*<br>weak | *formal policy integration and deliverable targets* | substantial micro-economic restructuring | *wider public education — future visions* | *round tables, stakeholder groups* |
| Stage 3: involvement<br>strong | binding policy<br>integration and strong international agreements | full economic evaluation;<br>green national and business accounts | curriculum integration;<br>local initiatives | community<br>in decision-making |

Table 4.1 shows that RBM is contributing to the implementation of SWM in various ways. But for each dimension of SWM (economic, social etc.), the achievement (in terms of how weak or strong the type of sustainability is implemented) varies. For instance, the economic dimensions of SWM, in RBM, is still very weak because there has only been a minor tinkering with economic instruments. On the other hand, RBM has made more progress on the political side of SWM because it is integrated in other policy plans and targets. An even stronger implementation of sustainability principles would involve the binding of policy integration to strong international agreements. From a social perspective, RBM principles have been pro-actively introduced in public education and roundtables. The move towards a more convincing implementation of sustainability in river basin management has thus involved not only education and better awareness but also the involvement of stakeholders in debates on these issues.

The implementation of RBM should also include actions that, for instance, focus on protecting the ecological integrity of the river. We are interested in examining how the various dimensions of SWM can be integrated in (systemic) water policies. This is what we will concentrate on in the next section.

## 4.3.1 Systemic tools for water management and monitoring

In Chapter 1, we saw how the various dimensions of water problems are inter-related. These interactions should be considered when we examine potential ways of managing water resources more sustainably. Using systems thinking could help us to make the transition towards SWM. The basis of a systems approach is to consider the various agents interacting in the world as systems. The challenge is to take uncertainty and complexity on board and to identify how a systems approach can shift a systemic understanding of water problems into a pro-active, policy orientated approach. What does this mean in practice? How could we shift 'systems thinking' into 'systems practice' in the context of water management?

○ If water managers were to use a systemic decision-making tool, in which ways do you think this would be helpful? (Note: this is a difficult question that many people interested in 'systemic' water management are trying to answer. You only have to think of ways in which the systems concepts you saw in Chapter 1 could be applied to water management.)

○ This tool could:

• help them identify the range of effects entailed by each decision, and *how these effects are linked*;

• clarify the *trade-offs* that are implicit in each strategic decision;

• assist the various organizations involved in defining their *goals and priorities* in a systemic way;

• make all *parts of the decision making process* clear and explicit and show how these are *linked*;

• ensure that systems practices are used as *learning tools* to help people understand what systems thinking is about and how it can help.

In fact, a systems methodology called **Sustainability Assessment Maps (SAMs)** has already been formulated and used, that can achieve all the outcomes listed above. It is a decision-aid tool which uses a systemic perspective to focus on the sustainability dimensions of potential projects.

SAMs are a graphic tool for representing information and assisting in decision-making. Each of the important dimensions in a compound problem is represented by an axis. Measurements of change or indications of priorities are mapped onto these axes. The resultant profile can be used to represent the current situation. Possible future scenarios or outcomes from the situation are then used to generate further profiles, which are themselves differentiated, so highlighting the trade-offs inherent in each possible choice. Another objective of a SAM is to give a global picture of all the different components of the problems at stake. Figure 4.4 shows a SAM for a new tidal barrage. Let us try to interpret what this map means and how it could help the situation.

Figure 4.4 shows that the wastes produced by the barrage are associated mainly with its construction phase. However, the barrage will also flood and destroy some mudflats in the estuary. These mudflats are extremely important breeding grounds for some rare species of birds as well as being the site of the last known colony of a species of endangered plant (Book 2, Chapter 4). This SAM then, gives a profile of high site sensitivity and high local ecological damage. The description of the non-local and long-term profile is also giving important messages: an estuary will be ecologically damaged. Even though it appears that other ecological sites will apparently not be affected, further assessment should be carried out to identify whether the damage caused to that single estuary could set any important precedent for the ecological health of the region. The decision must also take account of another constraint here, that of the operating and construction costs: barrages tend to be expensive to build initially and cheap to operate in the long run.

○ In your opinion, what are the advantages of representing potential projects in a SAM?

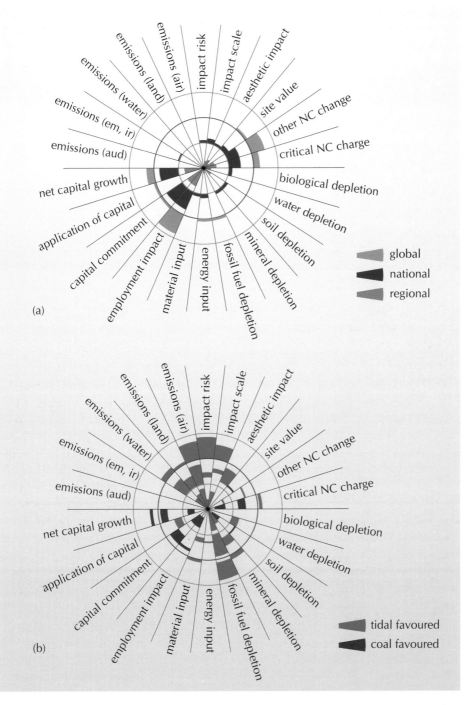

**Figure 4.4** The use of SAMs in the context of the construction of a new tidal barrage.

First, a SAM simplifies a situation by providing a clear, yet global representation of the issue. Building up the SAM is also a very useful learning exercise, because you have to review your understanding of the situation and highlight areas of uncertainty. Seeing the various types of impacts of the project simultaneously is also a much more realistic way to predict the outcomes. Though an easy thing to do, it is dangerous to focus on only one potential favourable outcome of the project while ignoring any possible adverse side effects.

Another systemic tool is a composite index called the **Water Poverty Index (WPI)**, which is used to monitor progress in the water sector. It has been developed by the Centre for Ecology and Hydrology in Wallingford (UK). Its construction has been based on the premise that monitoring water progress requires an interdisciplinary approach that may involve both qualitative and quantitative assessment techniques that should be integrated. The objective of this index is to help people understand how water can best be managed to meet their own needs and to assist water managers (who have to prioritize work activities and ensure progress is made) in their decision-making processes. The calculation of the index is based on the formulation of a framework (see Table 4.2), which incorporates a wide range of variables.

**Table 4.2**    The composite structure of the Water Poverty Index (WPI). (Source: Sullivan, 2002)

| WPI component | Examples of data used |
| --- | --- |
| *Resource (R):* measure of ground and surface water availability, adjusted for quality and reliability | assessment of surface and groundwater using hydrological techniques; quantitative and qualitative evaluation of reliability of resources (based on households survey) |
| *Access (A):* indicates the effective access people have to water for their survival | access to clean water as a percentage of households having a piped water supply (from households survey); access to sanitation as a percentage of population |
| *Use (U):* captures some measure of how water is used | agricultural water use expressed as [in terms of] a measure of irrigated land as a percentage of total cultivated land industrial use |
| *Capacity (C):* represents human and financial capacity to manage the system | membership of water user associations; water educational levels; water investment levels |
| *Environment (E):* captures an evaluation of ecological integrity related to water | percentage of households reporting erosion on their land; reports of crops loss during the last 5 years |

The scores of the WPI index are ranged on a scale from 1 to 100, with the score generated being a weighted additive value of the five major components[*]. There is built-in flexibility in the weighting given to the individual components and the choice of sub-components. The latter can be defined after consultation with stakeholders. Identifying the most appropriate and representative data for use as part of the WPI components constitutes an iterative process. The four main characteristics of the WPI tool have been described as follows:

- it is a tool for prioritization according to a standardized transparent method;
- it helps monitor progress over time;
- it empowers communities and decision-makers by giving them confidence in the rationale behind water management decisions;
- it is an evaluation tool to be applied at a variety of scales (national and community levels).

Both SAMs and the WPI provide simplified (but not simplistic) representations of complex water situations. For this reason, they constitute useful tools for various

[*] If $w_X$ is the weight applied to component X, then the WPI can be expressed as follows:

$WPI = (w_R R + w_A A + w_C C + w_U U + w_E E) / (w_R + w_A + w_C + w_U + w_E)$ The apparent simplicity of this equation is counter balanced by the complexity and subtlety in identifying which data and weightings should be used. This is done through consultative processes.

stakeholders to use when communicating about a specific complex water issue. They effectively allow people to 'map the debate' (by illustrating different possible scenarios, for instance, in the SAM), hence giving some transparency to the decision-making process. In this way they can:

- represent the inter-relations between the various components of a complex system;
- be constructed collectively as well as constituting a practical way of inviting participation both in debates and in decision-making.

This leads us to the next section, in which we will concentrate on various sustainability principles and so consider schemes for SWM.

# 4.4 The essential ingredients for a new governance of water

You have already examined the notion of governance in various environmental contexts previously in this course. 'Good' governance should:

- be transparent and accountable;
- have participatory mechanisms that reflect the local situation;
- respect the law and contractual obligations. #

Governance encompasses many interlinked social players and must be responsive to citizens needs in addition to the long-term sustainability of the natural resource base of the geographical area. Good water governance exists therefore where government agencies use legitimate policies, laws and an efficient administration to allocate and manage water resources.

As we continue our examination of good water governance and SWM, our assumption is that *good governance* is, in itself, one main ingredient for *putting sustainability into practice*.

## 4.4.1 The value of participation

The need for the participation of a variety of water **stakeholders** (Figure 4.5) in water management is becoming more and more important. This is influencing the way in which the 'water policies' of the future are being envisaged. At the International Conference on Freshwater in December 2001, the Secretary General, Hideaki Oda concluded that:

> The best phrase to sum up this conference would be *multi-stakeholder dialogue*. It would be a significant step towards the solution of water issues if we could establish dialogue at the 3rd World Water Forum among not only water experts but also among people *from all relevant fields*, such as poverty or finance.
>
> (Hideaki Oda, 2001)

This recent focus on the social dimension of water management reflects the fact that the water crisis is now understood as being mainly a **crisis in governance**: note that Oda describes the term 'multi-stakeholder dialogue' as the *best* phrase to sum up the whole conference — not 'water conflicts'; not 'water-related deaths; nor any other term! This is a very powerful conclusion.

(a)

(b)

(c)

**Figure 4.5** There are numerous and varied types of 'water stakeholders'. They range from 'experts' such as (a) water engineers, to (b) the workers who build walls and install water pumps, to (c) the children who help to collect water. Many more stakeholders take part, directly or indirectly, in the management of water resources.

The notion of 'participation' is central to that of good governance. We are now going to explore what it means in more practical terms, through a series of examples. Our first example concentrates on Water User Associations (WUA). WUAs contribute to a broadening of the debate on water management and participatory principles in various ways. They normally comprise a formal, legally-bound group of farmers (or other type of water users), often centred on a particular canal or water unit. The group is responsible for managing and maintaining the part of the water system that serves them. These associations have been set up as a result of central government determination (often with donor support), to devolve some of the responsibility for water, wastewater and irrigation onto the users. This initiative was motivated by the search for efficiency and costs-savings, so to that extent one could say that the creation of WUAs can be seen as a form of privatization. In this context, government agencies adopt the role of service provider rather than service operator. In this respect, WUAs are a type of community participation and community ownership of services. The degree of responsibility for the service and its maintenance varies from one model to another. In principle, their creation should lead to a greater commitment of the users and a reduction in governmental intervention. The 'devolving of responsibilities' to water users is aimed at empowering them much more and at inviting them not only to 'participate' but even, in some cases, to be in charge! This new system of governance closes, if not completely removes, the gap between those who control and those who use water. This means that, in new irrigation schemes for example, users should manage the investment directly.

Respecting customers' needs and knowledge can also be achieved using more demand-driven approaches. These concentrate on creating ways of using water more efficiently; because users know best how much they need, the type of environment in which they live, and the kind of technical and economic resources they have, they are also best placed to identify which system of water management will be most appropriate for them.

Greater participation in water management also arises from a recognition that civil society has in many practical instances initiated real improvements in RBM. NGOs, such as the 'Clean the Rhine' movement, the 'Young Water Action Team'* and many others, have changed river management policies and practices. Such examples can be powerful means of promoting this approach (Figure 4.6).

It is only with the reform of both **water institutions** and systems of water management, that it will be possible to integrate local knowledge and expertise in water management plans. More importantly, such governance can also help initiate a real political shift so that the value of neglected groups of stakeholders that are often silenced — such as minority indigenous groups or women — is recognized (Figure 4.7).

International Rivers Network

**Figure 4.6** Logo for International River Network.

(a)

(b)

(c)

**Figure 4.7** (a) Irrigated agriculture in terraces in the High Atlas in Morocco. (b) This 'water clock' is used in the far south of Morocco to allocate water to the various farmers of the village (Tata). This little bowl fills in three quarters of an hour, after which the flow of water in (c) the seguia (system of irrigation in narrow canals) is orientated in the direction of another field.

Thus, an increasing number of water managers are recognizing the value of **Indigenous Technical Knowledge (ITK)**. ITK is particularly important for basic water supply, sanitation and irrigation activities. It has been used throughout history (for example well-digging, gravity-fed ponds, irrigation works, control of seasonal flows by terracing, diversion, dams), and offers many cost-effective types of technology. Development professionals, who have developed parallel systems, without realizing that ITK systems existed, are now learning important lessons from ITK.

The position of *women* in water management is also interesting (Figure 4.8). Since the UN Decade for Women (1980–1990), women's multiple roles in development have been much more widely appreciated. Whereas they used to be seen primarily as *beneficiaries* of water services, they are now much more appreciated as water *actors*. In most developing countries, women are active in two heavy water-use sectors — agriculture and fisheries — as well as being exclusively responsible for managing

* The Young Water Action Team is a global movement of students and young water professionals, who aim to increase awareness, participation and commitment among young people in water-related issues.

**Figure 4.8** Women are important water stakeholders in developing countries.

water at the household level. Consequently, they may be more responsive to concerns regarding the long-term safe and sustainable use of water. In this way therefore, women are a key target group for messages on hygiene, water saving in agriculture, the need for water quality conservation and the protection of aquatic resources (Figure 4.8). As Jahan observed:

> Water management and water treatment in the western world is a field dominated by men, but in tropical developing countries women are the actual pace-makers for traditional water purification. As far as aid organizations have given any thought at all to the role of women in the context of new water supply projects, they have only been concerned with the time wasted and the hardship endured in fetching water from distant sources. But women are not just victims of the burden of providing water, they have been the source of knowledge and skills for providing safe water, and hence better health for rural areas.

> (Jahan, 1981)

The focus on the participation of people as stakeholders does not negate that on the ecological functions and economic dimensions of water issues. However, it enables a reassessment of the content, design and implementation of water policies. Acknowledging that professional 'water experts' are not the only stakeholders who can tackle water problems has shaken the way in which we approach water issues. This will be our focus in the following section.

## 4.4.2 Social learning and the construction of knowledge on water

Are official water experts better informed than the non-official water experts, who experience a variety of problems in their daily lives? Relations have been strained between the two types of community, but bridges between them are being built. Precious environmental knowledge and values are expressed through oral exchanges (story telling, public debates etc.), traditional practices, local legends and art (Box 4.1 and Figure 4.9). It is now clear that these are a valid source of information for environmental management and that participation should be broadened if valuable communication between these various stakeholders is to take place.

**Figure 4.9** The formulation and evolution of knowledge of water issues and the exchange of information on best water management practices, is conducted orally in many developing countries.

## Box 4.1. Poetry as an expression of local perceptions of water problems.

**Floods**

The poor live below, waiting for the river
to rise at night and take them to sea.
I've seen little cradles afloat, remains
of houses, chairs, and an august rage
of livid waters in which sky and terror are fused.
Its only for you, poor man, for your wife and offspring
for your dog and your tools, so that you can learn to beg.
The water doesn't rise to the homes of the gentlemen
whose snow-clad collars fly from the laundries.
Eat this devastating mud and these ruins that swim
with your dead, gently drifting to sea,
amid humble tables and lost trees
that tumble downstream displaying their roots.

(Pablo Neruda, 'Canto General')

A song by Daya Pawar, sang by women in Maharashtra (India), captures the anti-life force of the dammed river which irrigates commodity crops like sugarcane, while women and children thirst for drinking water.

As I build this dam
I bury my life.
The dawn breaks
there is no flour in the grinding stone.
I collect yesterday's husk for today's meal
the sun rises
and my spirit sinks.
Hiding my baby under a basket
and hiding my tears
I go to build the dam.
The dam is ready
it feeds their sugarcane fields
making the crop lush and juicy.
But I walk miles through forests
in search of a drop of drinking water
I water the vegetation with drops of my sweat
as dry leaves fall and fill my parched yard.

(In Shiva, V., 1989)

We usually learn about water issues through expert opinion in professional publications. Too often, the beneficiaries of water services, or the victims of water problems, do not perceive the whole water issue in the same way as these experts. The two poems in Box 4.1 focus on a type of vulnerability that we focused on earlier: the issue of poverty, in relation to the allocation of water resources. The construction of the dam, far from being perceived as a benefit and a source of improvement for the poor communities, is viewed as the end of hope, death even ('I bury my life'). The dam will not bring more water to the communities whose labour is used to build it; it will only benefit the richest members of society and the owners of export-crops (here sugarcane fields) whilst simultaneously damaging local ecosystems ('dry leaves fall and fill my parched yard'). Floods (as illustrated by Neruda) always damage the lives of the poor, who are abandoned by society and also, it would seem, destroyed by the forces of nature itself.

Accounting for the various types of knowledge about water issues is part of a general learning process; participatory processes in implementing sustainability start with participatory processes in learning. As a consequence, the concept of **social learning** has recently entered the discourse on environment and development issues. 'Social learning' takes place between different stakeholders in society (experts and non-experts, educationalists and students, etc.). Everybody learns from everybody. To facilitate 'social learning', institutions that can host such exchanges are needed. However, 'experts' rarely communicate with non-experts. Institutions that welcome stakeholders having different backgrounds and expertise, and that can facilitate communication between them by encouraging multi-directional learning and the formulation of trade-off policies are rare though. Here, open platforms like the WWW could perhaps prove helpful in hosting and facilitating debates that would otherwise not occur.

As Woodhill explains:

> Learning processes are processes by which society democratically adapts its core institutions to cope with social and ecological changes in ways that will optimize the collective well-being of current and future generations.

(Woodhill, 1998)

In the next section, we will focus on how water institutions could be reformed so that they allow participatory learning and policy process to take place.

### 4.4.3 Integrating water actions: the creation of partnerships

One of the premises of social learning is that the different types of stakeholders learn from each other. In this section, we will examine different types of partnerships that could facilitate this. Typically, in partnerships, various types of stakeholders or organizations are keen to co-operate in a common initiative.

The basis for advocating private sector–public sector partnerships is the (much challenged!) assumption that private commercial companies tend to operate services with greater efficiency and less waste than government run utilities. A further assumption is that the participation of the private sector in water policy also helps the formulation of new policy structures: instead of diminishing the role of the government, it could in fact change it by recommending a set of actions. These actions include compelling both public and private sector operators to obey set rules, or the establishment of an operating framework that could attract private sector and civil society involvement in providing water services (i.e. more diverse participation). However, as Chapter 2 showed, too great an involvement of the private sector can also have negative impacts on sustainable water management.

We have looked at various types of water stakeholders earlier in the chapter and now we are going to focus on four types of possible **water partnerships**:

- the community based and informal private sector;
- multilateral donors;
- professional partnerships;
- integrated institutions.

Each of these water partnerships will now be explored in turn below.

## The community based and informal private sector

Many governments have recently made new efforts to increase service coverage to poorer communities, whose domestic needs have not usually been met by the expansion of conventional water supply and sewerage schemes. These (mostly) rural schemes are frequently made possible by some development cooperation funds supplied by bilateral agencies such as the UN, the EU or by international NGOs. Their effectiveness often depends on the creation of partnerships with local community-based organizations, whether administrative entities such as Village Councils, or NGOs. Local NGOs and their international counterparts have attracted considerable attention in the recent past because of their effectiveness in reaching the poor, their knowledge and experience of working closely with communities, and their reputation of 'achieving much with little'.

## Multilateral donors

A number of international and national bodies offer research, funds and technical assistance in the course of development initiatives related to water. For instance, the member countries of the EU are among the largest donors to such initiatives through the newly created European Water Initiative. Within the UN system, a number of funds, programmes and specialized agencies have long been involved in some way with water related activity, usually by providing technical expertise or material assistance to different projects. By its declaration of an International Drinking Water Supply and Sanitation Decade (1981–90), the UN acted as a catalyst by promoting the international drive for improved basic water supply and sanitation services.

## Professional partnerships

Professional associations can mobilize their members to adopt and promote the ideas and actions proposed in the WWWs and frameworks for actions. An umbrella organization is needed for water, that builds on existing networks and could be formed under the auspices of the Global Water Partnership (GWP). Professional associations could also promote inter-disciplinary approaches. HELP (Hydrology for Environment, Life and Policy), for instance, adopts a new approach to hydrological problems by integrating three communities (scientists, water managers and policy-makers) as part of the UNESCO International Hydrology Programme. These are only a few examples amongst a plethora of 'water partnerships'.

Next, we are going to examine the institutional context in which these initiatives can take place.

### *Integrated institutions*

Earlier, we saw that new platforms (hosted, for instance, in the WWW) and partnerships (such as those we have just examined) could constitute institutional reforms which would allow the implementation of integrated and systemic thinking in water management. This is really becoming an imperative since currently, as Calder stresses:

> Our understanding of global water policy issues suffers from the extreme fragmentation of the field into national, regional, and local water authorities and a host of professional and scientific organizations established along sectoral lines. Until now, there has been no over-arching umbrella group able to deal with water policy issues in their entirety, identify problem areas, and advocate solutions.

(Calder, 1999)

An argument has been forwarded about what is required to create and strengthen existing institutions. In Chapter 1 we saw that the systemic dimensions of water issues affect the scale at which water institutions can operate. In the case of the creation of River Basin Organizations (RBOs), the GWP has suggested the following steps:

- design institutions acceptable to the formal and informal structures of the country;
- conduct appropriate fact-finding, awareness and negotiation campaigns;
- after bargaining and negotiating with the relevant stakeholders, develop an RBO network that provides incentives for integration and cooperation, and that can satisfy real and concrete interests of local people;
- involve all relevant stakeholders, as in Water Parliaments in France;
- provide a seed organization to initiate the development of agreed RBOs;
- equip RBOs with best management practices and appropriate legal powers, status, and the financial resources to carry out their responsibilities.

On a broader level, strengthening institutions might involve establishing some mechanisms for coordinating water uses at a national level, by the preparation of national water resource strategies and plans or by initiating laws that compel the integrated management of resources. An example here is the River Law of Japan (1997) that combines flood management, water supply and environmental management.

## 4.4.4 Political cooperation

In this section so far, we have examined the importance of **participatory water management** and social learning processes and how these can take place through the creation of appropriate partnerships and institutions. Now, we will investigate further some political dimensions of the new governance of water. We have already observed some reasons for potential water conflicts. Figure 4.10 illustrates how global water security can be threatened by water-related disputes.

In a political context, the sustainability of water management involves:

- a recognition of the importance of the value of water for human societies and for ecosystems;
- the need to allocate water for various needs in a fair way;
- the need to understand how water problems relate to economic problems (economic development, food production and international trade) and other environmental problems (e.g. climate change);
- the need to promote integrated institutions and cooperative arrangements between countries sharing the same water resource (river, lake etc.).

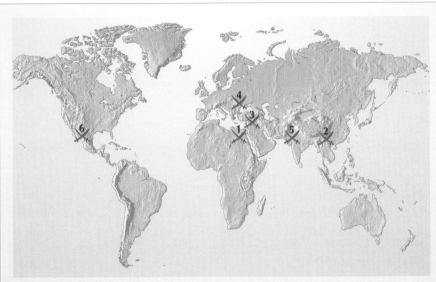

**Water** Some 261 river basins lie in more than one country, supporting over a third of the world's population. Global demand for drinking water has multiplied seven times during the 20th century, and is rising rapidly just as supplies are diminishing due to drought, pollution and over-abstraction. As Boutros Boutros-Ghali said, 'The next war in the Middle East will not be over oil but water'.

**How to defuse** As well as triggering conflicts, water has also been an unlikely source of peace between rivals, encouraging dialogue between, for example, Israel and Jordan, and Iran and Iraq. Is it too much to hope that our shared need for clean water might just trickle a little good sense into the minds of rivals?

**1 Nile** For years, civil war has prevented Sudan and Ethiopia from taking their full share of the river waters. Should this change, as seems likely, Egypt, 'the gift of the Nile', could face devastating shortages. It has already declared a willingness to go to war to defend the supply. And last year, the Kenyan parliament called on other east African nations to challenge Egypt's hold on the river. New institutions are being created to help the Nile countries cooperate in water management.

**2 Mekong** Shared by China, Vietnam, Thailand, Laos, Cambodia and Burma, the Mekong Basin is the source of growing regional tension, with China in particular planning developments that could severely restrict the flow to nations downstream. One way of tackling the issue has been to recreate an umbrella institution (The Mekong River Commission).

**3 Jordan** The ancestors of today's Israelis and Jordanians were tussling for control of the river in the pages of the bible: conflict over water has heightened tensions between Israel and the Palestinians.

**4 Tigris/Euphrates** Turkey, Iraq and Syria are increasingly at odds over dam plans and abstraction levels.

**5 Ganges/Indus** India and Pakistan — the sub-continent's nuclear neighbours — have competing claims to the waters of the Indus: while Indian control over the Ganges has sparked resentment, migration and ethnic conflict with Bangladesh.

**6 Colorado River Basin** This basin drains a vast area in the south-western United States and northern Mexico. During the past 50 years, this 1400 mile river has been tamed by a gigantic human plumbing system consisting of several dams, reservoirs, aqueducts and canals. Today, the domesticated river dispenses water for more than 20 million people in seven states. Six national parks along the river's shores support a multibillion-dollar recreation industry. The basic problem is that this basin includes some of the driest lands in the US and Mexico. For 100 years, there has been controversy and legal battles over how much of the water could be used by towns, ranchers, farmers, native Americans and Mexicans and how much should be left for wildlife. There is also controversy about water quality: as more water is withdrawn, the remaining flow gets saltier, so that the water reaching Mexico is so salty that it cannot be used for irrigation.

**Figure 4.10** A few examples of water-related disputes around the world.

Here, we are going to concentrate on this last issue of *political water cooperation*. Cosgrove has described this as having particular features:

> As mutual trust and confidence increase, and as issues appear that concern all parties and can be more effectively addressed through collective action, the level of co-operation gradually grows to a point where countries are willing to undertake joint action or allocate more significant resources.

(Cosgrove *et al.*, 2000)

Forty percent of the world's population occupies international river basins. An important aspect of the interdependence between countries within river basins, is that the industrial and agricultural development of one nation becomes the proper concern of another.

If upstream countries 'export' pollution and depleted fisheries, they impose environmental risks and economic burdens on those countries downstream hence increasing the risk of a water dispute escalating. So, collaboration must become an imperative:

> As countries sharing water resources have to deal with increasing scarcity and failing water quality, they will have to move towards closer collaboration or face escalating conflicts over resource allocation.

(Biswas et al., 1993)

You will recall the example of the Mekong river given earlier in this book (Table 2.3) and in your set book (*World Resources 2000–2001*, pp. 206–9). The river crosses some of the richest and some of the poorest South Asian countries (Cambodia, China, Lao, Myanmar, Thailand and Vietnam), whose governments are all very keen to promote economic development using the river's water. New economic developments (such as the construction of a dam and the diversion of the river) would threaten the traditional use of the waters as a source of fish and as a barrier to salt water penetration into the delta soils. In order to prevent conflicts, the Mekong River Commission was established in 1957. For four decades, political turmoil has hampered the Commission's effectiveness. But at the beginning of the 21st Century, the Basin countries are reaffirming their interest in working together and reinforcing the strength of this common institution. It is thus reassuring to observe that just as examples of water conflicts abound, those of political cooperation in water management are also growing in number (Box 4.2).

## Box 4.2  Water conflicts and cooperation in the Nile Basin

One famous example is the River Nile (Figure 4.11). It is the longest river in the world (6800 km) and is shared by nine countries with different climates, eco–systems and water needs. Upstream countries are not crucially dependent on the Nile waters; they can use rainwater for their agriculture. For the communities living and gaining livelihoods in the desert parts of Egypt and The Sudan however, the Nile remains a key economic resource. Sharing the Nile as a common resource has proved to be a very sensitive issue: historically it has given rise to serious disputes. The water conflicts here had two main aspects:

- conflicts were generated by the signature of provocative treaties concerning the river;
- conflicts were animated by two different approaches to water management: the comprehensive management approach of the colonial period and, in contrast, the approaches adopted by newly

**Figure 4.11**  The Nile river.

independent countries (which limited themselves to the management of their piece of river, in isolation from the rest of the river).

The governments of the Nile countries understand the strategic and critical nature of water resources and the danger that disagreements over water management could represent in terms of conflicts. Moreover, the political closeness between Egypt and the USA, at the time of some of the negotiations (1970s), was creating an unusual context (the USA being usually closer to Israel than Arab countries). If other riparian* countries chose to express their disagreements with Egypt too loudly, they would probably lose potential American investments and contribution to the development of the Nile basin. Clearly, political considerations were going to drive them to formulate common strategies.

The approach adopted by the Nile countries from the 1980s to avoid major disputes and deal collectively with some of the problems has focused on the creation of new institutions whose practices are based on cooperation between the riparian countries. These new institutions (through the Nile Basin Initiative) represent all the countries and try to accommodate their different interests, constraints and needs.

* Riparian countries: those who share the river with other countries.

The political dimension of SWM goes well beyond cooperation agreements between river basin countries and seems to be a necessary prerequisite if water management is to become more sustainable:

- At the global level, cooperation agreements to respect water, biodiversity and climate change targets, as well as the formulation of umbrella institutions and partnerships are all of a political nature. Furthermore, the need to integrate food security issues in water debates is economically *and* politically relevant.

- At a national and local level, the creation of partnerships and institutional set-ups that can encourage social learning processes are also political. In addition, pro-actively managing water resources in a way that respects the inter-dependencies between ecological and human systems also results from a very determined shift in political views. Finally, the allocation of water resources amongst users and uses is also a very political matter — one that often decides the richest and the poorest.

The political will to promote water initiatives that complement each other, in a systemic way, is, therefore, a crucial premise to the implementation of SWM.

## 4.5 Integrated Water Management

Earlier in this chapter, we examined what seemed to constitute useful ingredients to include in the formulation of a new system of water governance. These emerged from an initial discussion on what constitutes 'sustainable water management'. In this section, we are going to explore one particular response to the need for new systems of water management and governance, focused on Integrated Water Management (IWM). IWM seems so promising that it is becoming extremely popular. All the ideas are there, all sustainable principles can be respected. Now is the time to implement IWM, and let us examine why and how.

### 4.5.1 What is IWM?

Integrated Water Management (IWM) approaches water management in a way that encompasses all the known ingredients of sustainability. According to Calder:

> IWM involves the coordinated planning and management of land, water and other environmental resources for their equitable, efficient and sustainable use. IWM programmes need to be developed alongside, and not in isolation from economic structural adjustment and other sectoral programmes. For IWM strategies to be implemented, fragmentation of institutional responsibilities must be reduced.

> (Calder, 1999)

IWM objectives are based on the following principles:

1   Water has multiple uses and water and land must be managed in an integrated way.
2   Water should be managed at an appropriate level.
3   Water allocation should take account of the interests of all who are affected.
4   The ecological, economic, social and political dimensions of water should all be recognized.

Implementing IWM thus implies:

1   Leaving sufficient water in ecosystems to maintain proper functioning.
2   Protecting wetlands and floodplains to keep the benefits of seasonal flooding and provide storage for extreme flood flows.
3   Protecting and planting forests in upper river catchment areas, especially in mountainous areas.
4   Requiring full effluent treatment by industries and municipalities and applying **polluter-pays principles**.
5   Protecting water resources from agricultural run-off.
6   Creating groundwater protection zones.
7   Rehabilitating degraded areas to recover lost ecosystem functions (through re-forestation, wetland restoration, fish population restoration and so on).

IWM is now promoted in international conferences on water and well-known water institutions specifically focus on this approach (for example, the International Water Management Institute (IWMI) and the GWPs). NGOs have also been using the IWM approach in projects for some time. Interestingly, aside from general conceptual debates on how to integrate water related issues at a global scale, the implementation of IWM is mainly done at the project level.

At a global level, integrating economic, social and ecological dimensions of water management will take some time and considerable political effort. The allocation of water between water users and uses in a fair way might involve fundamentally questioning some major economic global agreements.

Now read the article *Water and sanitation interventions: The need for a more integrated approach* in the *Offprints for Block 4*. This article reminds us why we need integrated approaches.

● While reading this article, list the main reasons why we need an integrated approach.

● We need a better understanding of the combined effects of policies and actions and how they can be designed to satisfy local conditions. Improvements generated by the combination of actions are greater than the sum of effects of these actions. By focusing solely on one type of action, the links with other types of water interventions might be lost. Very often the objectives of one type of water action cannot be met until this water action is combined with another complementary initiative. The various dimensions of water problems are all inter-related as are the water actors.

In the next section, we look at how the move towards IWM practices can be initiated and encouraged, and by whom.

## 4.5.2  Constraints, catalysts and change agents in IWM

If IWM is a widely accepted solution to the water crisis, why is the water crisis still worsening? IWM has so far been implemented mostly at local, regional and occasionally national levels. A *global* implementation of IWM policies involves an extremely complicated integration of approaches and issues. A whole set of **constraints** is currently creating a blockage to the globalization of IWM practice.

Figure 4.12 shows the various practical contributors to a transition to SWM.

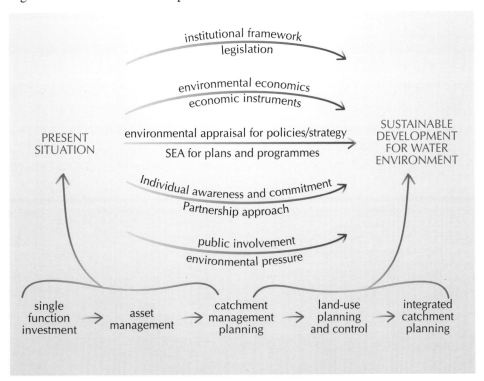

**Figure 4.12**  Sustainability in practice: the transition to IWM programmes.

● Using the information in Figure 4.12, list some potential obstacles to the global implementation of IWM.

**Table 4.3**  Activities that can help implementation of the World Water Vision strategy.

| Stakeholders | Policies | Institutions |
|---|---|---|
| International organizations, including private foundations. | Promote social and financial solidarity by sharing information on efforts to reduce the growing gap in access to safe water and environmental services between the rich and poor.<br><br>Promote transparency, accountability, and participation.<br><br>Promote **precautionary principle** in management of water risks. | Promote stable and fair food markets through the WTO.<br><br>Reform, strengthen and increase resources for the UN Agency Coordination.<br><br>Committee, Subcommittee of Water Resources (ACC-SWR).<br><br>Coordinate reform of water resource education to integrate environmental concerns through the International Hydrological Programme. |
| Governments, including government agencies and universities. | Facilitate mechanisms to allow management of land and water at the basin and catchment levels.<br><br>Adopt formal policy of full-cost pricing of water services.<br><br>Empower communities to develop their own water and sanitization systems based on their needs and willingness to pay.<br><br>Devise incentives (including pricing) to encourage sustainable water use.<br><br>Develop regulation that encourages the private sector while protecting the interests of society.<br><br>Accept limited sovereignty over water in international watercourses. | Dispel idea that water management is primarily a government responsibility.<br><br>Review structure and coordination mechanisms between water agencies to avoid conflicts and inefficiencies.<br><br>Promote transparency, accountability, and rule of law in all institutions.<br><br>Assign responsibility and resources for municipal water supply and sanitation to the city or community level.<br><br>Establish participatory market processes for water allocation. |
| Private sector, local and international. | Be responsible to society as well as to shareholders. | Foster community representation in corporate governance structure. Include an ethics subcommittee. |
| Nongovernmental organizations and communities. | Accept primary responsibility for water; be guardians of water resources; delegate upward only what cannot be managed locally (subsidiarity principle). | Participate in management of water supply and irrigation schemes. |

- Here are some of the general constraints:

- water institutions should be reformed in order to change the policy making process;
- the way in which we identify, perceive and understand environmental problems (not only water problems) should be more systemic;
- economic, political, legal and personal *incentives* should be more carefully formulated and communicated.

At a global level, these could constitute important constraints: the reform of international institutions, for instance, or changing economic incentives at a global, international

**Table 4.3**   (continued)        Research and development and Investments.

| Stakeholders | Research and development | Investments |
|---|---|---|
| International organizations, including private foundations. | International water and environmental standards setting and national monitoring, with ACC-SWR in the lead and with biannual reporting through World Water Development Report.<br><br>Innovative research of institutional research and technological approaches to better water management. | Training and education on integrated water resource management.<br><br>International monitoring of water availability, quality, and productivity.<br><br>Provide loans only when sustainable integrated water resource management policies are in place. |
| Governments, including government agencies and universities. | Nationally adapted water research management programmes.<br><br>National laboratory testing and certification of safe biotechnology for food production and waste treatment.<br><br>Systematic data collection and reporting on water resource availability, renewal rates, quality, and uses.<br><br>Extensive training and credit systems for small holder farms. | Capacity building, including redundancy payment for marginal staff and appropriate salary structure for public agencies.<br><br>Public goods such as flood protection, with the public sharing pollution control cost.<br><br>Targeted subsidies to low-income and disadvantaged groups to satisfy basic needs for water, sanitization, and hygiene. |
| Private sector, local and international. | Water-saving technologies.<br><br>Desalination.<br><br>Safe biotechnology for food production and waste treatment. | Urban water supply and domestic and industrial wastewater treatment.<br><br>Irrigation systems.<br><br>Water storage. |
| Nongovernmental organizations and communities. | Regional and global networking to share community-based solutions. | Rainwater harvesting.<br><br>Household-based water supply and sanitation.<br><br>Community microcredit schemes. |

level, is a massive enterprise, which will take a while to succeed! In contrast with these constraints and at more manageable geographical scales, there are some catalysts which could accelerate the move towards a sustainable management of natural resources. Thus:

- some stakeholders have unique valuable practical knowledge about water issues;
- some examples of best practice already exist and a consideration of these should be a part of the development of new systems of sustainable IWM.

Table 4.3 gives you a full range of **catalysts** — i.e. types of actions — that could promote the implementation of IWM.

**Patron in Chief:
Nelson Mandela**

**Figure 4.13** Change agents and catalysts. The Working for Water Programme in South Africa and the Water Research Fund for Southern Africa have both been promoting new integrated approaches towards water management.

○ From this table, select one type of action and explain the extent to which it is a catalyst. Identify other types of actions and types of progress towards IWM that it could trigger.

○ In the third column, under 'Institutions', the following recommendation can be found: 'Review structure and co-ordination mechanisms between water agencies to avoid conflicts and inefficiencies'. This would be an important 'catalyst' to promote better (integrated) water management because the lack of integration that is often observed in current water policies is, to a large extent, due to fragmented, sectoral, institutions that do not work together and cannot learn from each other. Incentives aimed at encouraging SWM constitute another important catalyst: if water consumption habits do not change, the management of the resource, as a whole, will not change either.

At the beginning of this section, we examined how both constraints and catalysts can have an effect on the movement towards sustainable management of water resources. Now, we are going to concentrate on **change agents**. Change agents are people (or institutions) who are charged with, or volunteer for, introducing change in a policy process. In the context of organizations, change agents are often described as entrepreneurs or champions and they are very important in water management, owing to the complex nature of issues where institutions and incentives do not always exist to promote integrated SWM.

○ Looking at Table 4.3. find some examples of change agents.

○ NGOs and communities are listed in the 'stakeholders' column. Some NGOs have been real change agents through the exceptional initiatives they have taken (for example, the 'International Rivers Network' and the 'Clean the Rhine' movement mentioned earlier in this chapter). Governments can also be change agents in water management: the Working for Water Programme (WWP), is a good example of innovative action taken by the South African government. Even universities can be change agents as a result of their research-related activities.

One famous example of such IWM practice is the WWP in South Africa (see Figure 4.13).

○ In your opinion, what are the most positive and promising characteristics of the WWP? Could it inspire the creation of other, similar programmes?

○ The WWP is truly integrated because it tackles environmental, political, social and ecological issues simultaneously. It is fully supported by the South African Government, which also gives it financial backing. A variety of stakeholders have been empowered through working to implement the programme itself, or by contributing to its improvement (through research, or within the legal system). Although the water actions involved here have been varied, they have been linked to each other. New environmental laws could indeed inspire neighbour or other countries and so become a catalyst for global improvement in water practices and institutions.

Various systems approaches, including multiple cause diagrams, can aid the identification of constraints, catalysts and change agents, as well as demonstrate how they contribute to the implementation of a water programme.

Now go to the web and complete the activities associated with Chapter 4.

# 4.6 Conclusion

In this chapter, we focused on what sustainability means in the context of water management. Various definitions of water sustainability, based on the ecological, economic, social and political dimensions of water issues were examined. The principles that underlie Sustainable Water Management were identified and we looked briefly at the way in which systems tools can help in the transition to SWM. We identified participatory and social learning processes, partnerships and political cooperation as key ingredients for a new system of governance of water issues. Although they are difficult to integrate into systems of water management, because these need reforming, they do constitute some real 'catalysts', i.e. some factors that can help in implementing change. Some people, or institutions, can also have the effect of change agents and through the initiatives they take, and the ways in which they inspire other stakeholders, they help the spread of new systems of SWM.

We then examined how Integrated Water Management can help in putting SWM into practice. IWM, a popular new approach to water management, is seen as encapsulating all the principles and criteria needed when implementing SWM. It is one of the initiatives and analytical frameworks that constitute the 'transition towards SWM, as shown in Figure 4.14.

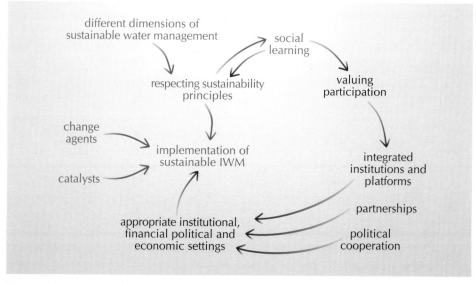

**Figure 4.14** Multiple cause diagram: towards sustainable IWM.

A major conclusion is that we need to think about water in a new, more systemic way, and we need to examine how water issues relate to other environmental ones. This new way of thinking needs to be accompanied by the creation of a new professionalism of water management that includes the skill to facilitate exchanges on water knowledge amongst various stakeholders within new institutional platforms (including the WWW).

In this chapter, we advocated the pro-active implementation of SWM in order to address the 21st century water crisis. The situation, already worrying, will deteriorate if we do nothing to improve the way in which we manage water issues, as the World Water Council (part of the World Water Vision) has shown in the following three scenarios.

- *Business as usual*: a continuation of current policies and extrapolation of trends.
- *Technology, economics and business sector:* private initiatives lead research and development; globalization drives economic growth; the poorest are left behind.
- *Values and lifestyles*: sustainable development, with an emphasis on research and development in the poorest countries.

The main forces affecting the global water scenarios are population and economic growth, demographic change, technological change, social trends and environmental quality. The development and discussion of qualitative scenarios provided a platform for consultation among many stakeholders with different backgrounds and perspectives. This reinforces the assumption that, for water problems to be solved, we not only need to understand the water crisis in all its dimensions, but we also need to ensure that the various types of water stakeholders communicate and share knowledge and experiences.

## 4.7 Summary of Chapter 4

4.1     The sustainability of the water environment has various inter-related dimensions. Its terms of reference are as follows:

- The retention of sufficient water within the natural systems to provide a host of valued environmental goods and services and ecosystems functions.
- The economic dimensions of sustainable development, which shift the emphasis towards the fair allocation of available water and the development of least-cost supply enhancement schemes.
- The social dimension of sustainability: all consumers should be able to take enough water to satisfy their basic needs and maintain their livelihoods.

Behind each of these dimensions lie another (very important) one: the *political* will to consider each of these dimensions as equally important in SWM.

4.2     The seven sustainability criteria identified by Gleick can be used to indicate whether sustainability is being implemented through water management policies or not.

4.3     Systemic representations (such as Sustainability Assessment Maps) illustrate the inter-relations between the components of a complex system. They can be constructed collectively, hence inviting participation in debates and in decision-making.

4.4     Integrated Water Management involves the co-ordinated planning and management of land, water and other environmental resources for their equitable, efficient and sustainable use.

4.5     The advantages of participatory processes in the formulation of water responses are numerous and include, the devolving of certain responsibilities and the sharing of knowledge on best management practices.

4.6     Social learning implies that our water knowledge could be improved if the expert/non-expert divide was lifted and if communication was improved between the two groups of stakeholders.

4.7     Partnerships allow different water actors to work together: examples include private–public and professional as well as public sector–informal private sector partnerships.

4.8 To implement new principles of water governance, institutional reforms are needed.

4.9 Institutions cannot be reformed if there is no political will to do so.

4.10 Political cooperation is needed to provide long term solutions to water conflicts.

4.11 Change agents are people (or institutions) who are designated or volunteer to introduce change. Catalysts (such as new laws) also lead to change.

## Learning Outcomes for Chapter 4

When you have completed this chapter you should be able to:

4.1 Define and use, or recognize definitions and applications of, each of the terms given in **bold** in the text. (Question 4.1)

4.2 Giving examples, explain why ecological, economic, social and political dimensions of water issues all need to be taken into consideration in sustainable water management plans. (Questions 4.1 and 4.2)

4.3 Explain what the current problems are in the governance of water management and give some examples of what a better system of water governance would include. (Questions 4.3, 4.4, 4.5 and 4.6)

4.4 Discuss, citing examples, how integrated water management may be implemented. (Questions 4.7 and 4.8)

## Questions for Chapter 4

### Question 4.1

After having examined the various dimensions of sustainable water management, as well as the ingredients for a new system of water governance, describe the main characteristics of a SWM policy.

### Question 4.2

What are the seven water sustainability criteria identified by Gleick?

### Question 4.3

Give some examples of stakeholders whose voice has rarely been taken into account in water management.

### Question 4.4

Give some examples of water partnerships.

### Question 4.5

Why is institutional reform a critical ingredient for sustainable water management?

### Question 4.6

Why is political cooperation and will a critical ingredient for sustainable water management?

## Question 4.7

What does IWM mean?

## Question 4.8

Give one example of a change agent and one example of a catalyst that promoted IWM.

# References

Biswas, A. K. et al. (eds) (1993)*Water for Sustainable Development in the 21st Century.* Delhi: Oxford University Press.

Calder, I. R. (1999) *The Blue Revolution. Land use and integrated water resources management.* London: Earthscan.

Cosgrove, W. J. and Rijsberman, F. R. for the World Water Council (2000) *World Water Vision. Making water everybody's business.* London: Earthscan.

Gleick, P. (ed.) (1993) *A guide to the world's freshwater resources.* Oxford: Oxford University Press.

Jahan, S. A. (1981) *Traditional water purification in tropical developing countries.* West Germany: GTZ.

Miller, G. T. (1998) (10th edn) *Living in the environment. Principles, connections and solutions.* Belmont, CA: Wadsworth.

Neruda P. (2000) (50th anniversary edition) The poem Flood in Canto general of Chile, Section VII. Berkeley: University of California Press, p. 221.

Oda, H. (2001) *A vision of water for food and rural development.* World Water Forum.

Pearce, D. (ed.) (1993) *Blueprint 3: measuring sustainable development.* London: Earthscan.

Shiva, V. (1989) *Staying Alive.* London: Zed Publications.

Sullivan, C. (2002) *Using the water poverty index to monitor progress in the water sector.* London: CEH Wallingford, DFID.

Woodhill, J. and Roling, N. (1998) The second wing of the eagle: the human dimension in learning our way to more sustainable futures, in Roling and Wagemakers (eds), *Facilitating sustainable agriculture. Participatory learning and adaptive management in times of environmental uncertainty.* Cambridge: Cambridge University Press, pp. 46-72.

# Answers to Questions for Chapter 1

## Question 1.1

*Virtual water* is 'hidden' in that it is used in the production of agricultural and industrial products.

*Water stress* is an indicator of insufficient water of satisfactory quality or quantity to meet human and ecosystems needs. Water stress begins when there is less than $1700\,m^3$ per person a year for all major functions (domestic, industrial, agricultural, and natural ecosystems). It becomes severe when there is less than $1000\,m^3$ per capita.

*Water availability* Water that is available, is not scarce or polluted and can therefore be directly used.

*Water responses* include a set of varied types of initiatives aimed at addressing the water crisis.

*Water systems* can refer to the physical hydrological cycle (in that it is made of different interacting parts) or to the way in which the economic, political, social and ecological dimensions of water issues are all inter-related.

## Question 1.2

A few examples of water initiatives include data collection, modelling, water campaigns and education, traditional irrigation techniques, self help credit systems for water management issues, restoration of ecosystems, investments and water engineering projects. Their objective is to contribute to solving water problems and they can do so in various ways. The various initiatives we explored in this chapter take place at different geographical scales (from world to regional and local levels), over different periods of time (some are limited to a short-term project, some extend over many years). They either involve very limited groups of stakeholders (in a village, for instance) or a network of participants from around the world (e.g. in research, modelling or data collecting projects).

## Question 1.3

The second and third World Water Fora, in The Hague and Kyoto, took place respectively in March 2000 and March 2003. The Water Dome was organized in parallel to the World Summit on Sustainable Development, in the summer of 2002. The international dimension of these events illustrates a global recognition of the water crisis as well as a global will to address it.

## Question 1.4

Water availability can be affected by water scarcity or water pollution. Water scarcity is due, in many parts of the world, to climatic differences and climate change (e.g. in Africa and certain parts of North America). It can also be caused by water over-abstractions. This, in itself, can take place because:

- the climate is too arid (e.g. Africa);
- abstracting water helps meet the needs of growing populations (e.g. Asia);
- the water needs to be transferred to where growing populations actually settle (e.g. mega urban centres in Latin America);
- economic activities are increasing (e.g. in Europe);
- ecological equilibrium is upset and the destruction of forest ecosystems increases run-off (e.g. Asia and the Pacific).

On top of this, water availability can also be affected by the fact that the little water that is not abstracted (from groundwater for instance) is polluted and therefore cannot be used as it is (e.g. North America). For this reason, while it is not 'scarce', it is 'not available' because it is unsafe to use.

All these negative factors can also be combined, so jeopardizing water availability even further.

## Question 1.5

China, India, and the US. If densities of population are taken into account, then water problems appear clearly: there is not enough water available *per capita*. An important lesson can be drawn from this: depending on how water information (data) is provided, the general message one gets can be very misleading. In the context of water, it is therefore important to take account of the density of population.

## Question 1.6

380 000 litres are needed to make a car, while it takes 100 litres to produce 1 kg of paper. Importing a tonne of wheat by implication also imports 1000 tonnes of water that have been needed to produce it.

## Question 1.7

The main issues addressed deal with the lack of access to sanitation (that affects 2.4 billion people in the world), as well as a desperate need to invest in water initiatives that are respectful of systemic approaches to water management (such as IWM). The EU, for instance, has invested €1.4 billion for water projects in its new European Water Initiative.

## Question 1.8

Disputes focused on water diversion and hydro-electricity between countries sharing the River Danube. Mexico and the United States had important disagreements concerning the salinization and agrochemical pollution of the Rio Grande: this was caused by intensive agricultural activities in the US, the effects of which were suffered further south, in Mexico.

## Question 1.9

The hydrological cycle collects, purifies and distributes the Earth's fixed supply of water, powered by solar energy and gravity.

## Question 1.10

Urban sanitation systems, Integrated Water Management and River Basin Management are all examples of systemic approaches to water management. The first one respects the principle of the 'dual function' of water (i.e. providing clean water to the citizens and taking away their waste) and allows the transformation and circulation of water from dirty to clean water. IWM pays special attention to taking all dimensions of water issues and all water stakeholders into account when organizing the management of the resource. RBM concentrates on the systems boundaries to be considered when managing the resource.

# Answers to Questions for Chapter 2

## Question 2.1

*Ecosystem functioning*

By saying that ecosystems 'function', what we mean is that transfers of materials occur between their various components (Book 2, Chapter 1). If an ecosystem is 'healthy' and 'in equilibrium', it survives shocks (perturbations) and all is well! A healthy ecosystem has the capacity (through its natural processes and components) to provide goods and services that could be used or are being used to improve the quality of human life. Thus, ecosystems provide goods and services; they have the capacity to abate pollution (up to a certain point) generated by our activities; they provide our life support and contribute to the maintenance of our mental and physical health.

*Point and non-point sources of water pollution:*

Point sources discharge pollutants at specific locations through pipes, ditches or sewers into water. Pollution from non-point (diffuse) sources cannot be traced to any one site of discharge. They are usually large land areas that pollute water by run-off, or depositions from the atmosphere. The distinction between these two types of pollutants is connected with the monitoring and regulation of water pollution: while point sources are easy to identify, being located at specific places, diffuse pollution is more of a problem. This highlights the need to prevent water pollution, since repairing and/or stopping the damage resulting from it might be particularly difficult.

*Eutrophication*

This is the process by which an ecosystem (often aquatic) increases in productivity as a result of an increase in the rate of nutrient input. The nutrients here include the nitrogen and phosphorus found in sewage and agricultural run-off. They stimulate blooms of algae and other plants, which consume large quantities of oxygen at night and eventually remove even larger quantities of oxygen from the water when they die and decompose. The effects of low oxygen concentrations in the water are particularly conspicuous when this causes a massive fish kill.

*Acidification*

Acidification can be described as an increase, over time, in the level of acidity in a system, accompanied by a decrease in the 'acid neutralizing capacity' of that system. The effects of acid rain, for instance, can be seen in damaged forests.

*Water engineering*

The term 'water engineering' describes one specific way of dealing with water problems: it focuses on the construction of water infrastructures (dams, pipes and canals; desalination plants etc.) and the reliance on technology to meet water needs. Its main objective is to increase the supply of water, either by increasing the quantity of water that can be directly used, or by purifying the available water source(s).

## Question 2.2

Humans cannot live without water: their reliance on water is as basic a need as the need to breathe. They are, therefore, vulnerable to water shortages, since they need water both for direct consumption and to produce food. They are also vulnerable to phenomena such as floods: too much water can destroy human settlements or spread water-related diseases. Our methods of managing water resources can decrease or even increase this vulnerability — especially if water allocation is unequal. In addition, all humans are vulnerable in that they cannot easily choose where their water supply originates: if you live in the Amazon forest, you will benefit from an abundance of water. If you were born in an area of the planet that is arid, you will have to learn how to deal with water scarcity.

## Question 2.3

Humans are fragile beings: their life depends not only on water but also on *safe* water. Although human societies have developed ways of treating polluted water, they currently seem unable to reduce the levels of pollution they are themselves generating. The effects of polluted water can cascade from damaging human health (when polluted water is directly ingested or indirectly used to produce food) to generating disruptions in ecosystem functioning (if pollution cannot be abated by ecosystem functioning). When ecosystems are damaged, not only is the natural treatment of pollution reduced or even halted, but the life support and amenity functions of ecosystems are similarly affected.

## Question 2.4

3 to 4 million people die of water-related diseases each year. The term water-related disease is often used loosely to describe all diseases carried by water. Strictly speaking, 'water-borne diseases' are those in which the infectious agent is itself carried by water (the cholera-causing organism, for instance). Other diseases are 'water washed'. These include skin diseases such as scabies; they can also be 'eater related' (in which case the disease is spread via an organism living in water, that is part of the diet — e.g. schistosomiasis which is carried by snails). They may also be 'insect related' (in which case they are spread by an insect which lives in or near water — e.g. malaria which is carried by mosquitoes, whose larval and pupal stages are aquatic). Many water diseases are spread by poor sanitation.

## Question 2.5

The first type of ecosystem service ('source') refers to its ability to provide us with goods (quantity of water, fish, etc.) and services (recreation, fisheries, etc.). Ecosystems can also act as 'sinks' and abate (dilute, for instance) pollution. They also provide us with a habitat within which we can live. The various biological and chemical processes carried out in ecosystems result in the creation of an environment within which we can live. Finally, not only we can survive thanks to the life support functions but our health (physical and mental) is maintained thanks to the fourth type of ecosystem service: healthy ecosystems provide us with clean safe water as well as a beautiful environment within which to live.

## Question 2.6

Infrastructure developments and land conversion are two examples of ways in which aquatic ecosystems can be badly damaged. Thus, for instance, aquatic ecosystems as a 'source' can be altered because these human activities change the timing and quantity of river flows. Similarly, our life support can also be damaged by these activities because habitats are destroyed.

## Question 2.7

Affecting one type of function (and or service) can alter another type of function (and or service): for instance, over-abstracting water (hence affecting the source functions) will decrease the ability of ecosystems to dilute pollution and hence perform the sink functions. This, in turn, will affect the habitat and its amenity (3rd and 4th functions).

## Question 2.8

The UK 'water sector' includes various types of stakeholders. Some of them are 'specialized in water': they include the 'water industry', itself comprized of the water companies (specialized in distributing and treating the resource) and the water regulators (the Drinking Water Inspectorate and OFWAT). It also involves water 'actors' that are specialized in water, such as the Environment Agency, English Nature, various NGOs such as Water Aid or Tear Fund, as well as a plethora of other stakeholders (farmers, etc.) who are all involved one way or another in the management of water.

## Question 2.9

The privatization of water companies was supposed to increase the efficiency with which water services and the resource itself are managed. But the companies have often shown that they are not prepared to invest enough to meet their objectives, and so the customers, in some situations, have not received what was promised to them.

## Question 2.10

Water engineering, for a long period of time, succeeded in meeting water needs by increasing the supply of water. Numerous examples of water engineering can be described as real proofs of human ingenuity, and they helped improve health and sanitation, for instance. But the shortcomings of water engineering are also becoming evident, in particular when the size of the enterprize is too large. The problems arise when the construction of a large dam, or the channelization of a river, for example, go against the functioning of aquatic ecosystems and the welfare of human communities; even though the supply of water seems to be increased, the biodiversity and health of the ecosystems might have been so damaged that the quality of the water decreases, hence reducing the overall availability of the resource. It can be said then, that water engineering responses, even when planned at a large scale, do not tend to take into account all the dimensions (ecological, social, political as well as economic) of the water problems they are addressing. This is proving to be more and more problematic.

## Question 2.11

Sectoral approaches of water management only consider one dimension of the water problems (for instance biodiversity loss in the aquatic ecosystem, or pollution of the water by pesticides, or over-abstraction, etc.). Formulating a 'sectoral solution' to address a complex, multi-dimensional water problem, will not be helpful in the long run, since many dimensions of the problems will still remain. In order to move away from sectoral, 'partial' policies, we need to involve more stakeholders in the management of the resource, and integrate various approaches.

# Answers to Questions for Chapter 3

## Question 3.1

Water is a global resource: it is everywhere on our 'blue planet'. The global dimensions of water issues very much refer to its systemicity — i.e. the way in which the hydrological cycle works, at the level of the planet, the way in which economic policies (for instance in agricultural plans) may affect ecological systems (for instance if too much water is 'exported' through exports of agricultural products), the way in which political decisions may affect human and ecological health in different regions (for instance when these political decisions refer to the management of a shared river). The global dimensions of water problems therefore refer to the physicality of these (systemic) inter-dependencies.

The term 'water globalization' has been used in this chapter to describe various forms of management, understanding, monitoring and governance of the resource.

## Question 3.2

Global Water Markets have been shown to favour the commodification of water resources to the extent that this resource is now considered as any other good to be traded in a liberalized way across the globe. This has presented important environmental and social problems and water needs seem to be unsatisfactorily met because of the institution of global water markets. On the other hand, these are supposed to make the management of water more efficient, but there is still a long way to go to achieve this objective, if it is to be achieved through water markets.

## Question 3.3

International water laws are needed to help monitor, manage and regulate water management as well as helping in resolving water conflicts. This is because it seems very difficult to conciliate laws from different countries when the issue at stake is a shared common resource (for instance, a river). The harmonization of water laws, however, seem to take a long time to be happening and this contrasts with the urgency of the water crisis currently experienced in the world.

## Question 3.4

Global water networks introduce a new form of water governance, aimed at increasing participatory processes and exchanges of information and practices. More and more global water networks are being developed on the WWW, hence by-passing constraints presented by more traditional forms of institutions. The range of stakeholders (i.e. their nationalities, backgrounds, professions, political allegiance, etc. ) involved can therefore be extremely varied. Enlarging the boundaries of 'water debates' and 'learning platforms' is a way of taking better account of the global dimensions of water issues.

They will work better if all types of stakeholders (not only experts and government) can have access to these new types of platforms. However, despite the apparent openness of such networks, barriers such as the 'digital divide' are still very much at work.

## Question 3.5

The Institut de Droit International (institute of international law), the International Law Association (ILA) and the International Law Commission (ILC) of the United

Nations are working at defining international laws and at protecting the notions of *equitable water use* and the protection of the *benefits* provided by watercourses.

## Question 3.6

The Water Framework Directive expands the scope of water protection to all waters and sets clear objectives that a 'good status' must be achieved for all European waters by 2015 and that water use must be sustainable throughout Europe. The WFD has set intermediary targets from now until 2015.

## Question 3.7

Dialogue on food, water and the environment; the Global Water Partnership; the Virtual Water Forum, Streams of Knowledge (etc.) are all examples of global water networks on the web. Because these platforms are on the Web, they allow stakeholders from all over the world to communicate and share their knowledge and experience. The Web dimension also allows both a certain spontaneity and an ease of access to the fora.

# Answers to Question for Chapter 4

## Question 4.1

Sustainable water management involves preserving the ecological integrity of water supply systems, wasting less water, allowing fair access to water supplies, and giving people a say in how water resources are developed and used (i.e. participatory decision-making). The formulation of an SWM policy will involve the consultation of various stakeholders. This consultation process might be facilitated by a change agent or a catalyst. The consultation process will take place in the context of a new 'platform'; open to a variety of stakeholders that includes non-experts.

## Question 4.2

The seven principles are as follows:

- A minimum water requirement should be guaranteed to all humans to maintain their health (economic and social dimensions).
- Sufficient water should be guaranteed to restore and maintain the health of ecosystems (ecological dimensions of SWM).
- Data on water resources availability, use, and quality should be collected and made accessible to all parties (economic and social dimensions of SWM).
- Water quality should be maintained to certain minimum standards (social, economic and ecological dimensions).
- Human actions should not damage the long term renewability of freshwater (social, economic and ecological dimensions of SWM).
- Institutional mechanisms should be set up to prevent and resolve conflicts over water (economic and social dimensions of SWM).
- Water planning and decision-making should be democratic, ensuring representation of all affected parties and fostering direct participation of affected interests (economic and social dimensions of SWM).

## Question 4.3

These types of stakeholders are typically un-heard by water experts who, for a long time, did not value their knowledge; they include indigenous people and women, for instance (mostly in developing countries). Although for a long time these stakeholders were considered as non-experts on water, they are now seen as being able to contribute greatly to the formulation of policies that are locally more appropriate to social and ecological needs.

## Question 4.4

There are different types of water partnerships; the idea is to make stakeholders who normally don't work together, unite around one activity or policy. Thus, the private sector can join the public sector and the local community based organizations can be supported by the public sector.

## Question 4.5

Existing institutions are very specialized and sectoral. Sustainable water management requires more integration of all the dimensions of water issues and will therefore require institutional reforms.

## Question 4.6

Political cooperation is a necessary ingredient for sustainable water management because so many rivers are shared by countries that could compete for the resource, hence generating potential water conflicts. Political will and agreements are the basis for any institutional and paradigm reform.

## Question 4.7

IWM involves the co-ordinated planning and management of land, water and other environmental resources for their equitable, efficient and sustainable use. IWM programmes need to be developed alongside economic structural adjustment and other sectoral programmes and the fragmentation of institutional responsibilities must be reduced.

## Question 4.8

One of the water targets that emerged from the World Summit on Sustainable Development (August 2002), committed governments to implement IWM by 2005. This is also an important catalyst in the move towards more sustainable water management.

# Acknowledgements

Grateful acknowledgment is made to the following sources for permission to reproduce material in this book:

## Chapter 1

*Figure 1.2*: United Nations, www.johannesburgsummit.org; *Figure 1.3*: UNEP GEO Team. Reproduced by permission UNEP www.umep.org/geo3; *Figure 1.4*: Courtesy of Steve Hawthorn; *Figure 1.5*: National Geographic magazine (2002) September, **202**, No. 3, pp. 14-15; *Figure 1.7*: Courtesy of Steve Hawthorn; *Figure 1.11a, b*: © Peter Solness.

## Chapter 2

### Table

*Table 2.1*: Tyler Miller Jr., G. (1998) 'Water Pollution' Living in the Environment, 10th edn, Thomson Learning Global Rights Group; *Table 2.3*: Adapted from Daily (1997) in IUCN (2000) p.44.

### Figures

*Figure 2.1a*: Le Hoai Phuong/ UNEP/ Still Pictures; *Figure 2.1b*: Courtesy of Sandrine Simon; *Figure 2.2*: Courtesy of Mike Dodd; *Figure 2.3a*: ©Robert Brook/Science Photo Library; *Figure 2.3b*: Hartmut Schwarzbach/ UNEP Still Pictures; *Figure 2.4*: Courtesy of Sandrine Simon; *Figure 2.5a*: (Rhine) Thomas Raupach/ Still Pictures; *Figure 2.5b*: (Italy) Mark Edwards/Still Pictures; *Figure 2.6*: (Worcester) Stewart Writtle Stringer/AP; *Figure 2.6b*: (Bangladesh) Pavel Rahman, Stringer/AP; *Figure 2.6c*: (Prague) Rene Volfik/AP, CTK; Figure 2.8: Courtesy of Mike Dodd; *Figures 2.8, 2.9, 2.10*: Courtesy of Mike Dodd; *Figure 2.11*: Trygve Bolstad/ Panos Pictures.

## Chapter 3

### Text

*Box 3.1*: Poupeau, F. (2002) Water Privatisation in La Paz (Bolivia): Lyonnaise des Eaux dominates the scene, Le Monde Diplomatique.

### Figures

*Figure 3.1*: Rob Cousins/Panos Pictures; *Figure 3.2*: © Debra Ferguson/AG Stock/Science Photo Library; *Figure 3.3*: Courtesy of Jim Frederickson; *Figure 3.4*: Reproduced by permission. Copyright © European Communities. www.europa.eu.int; *Figure 3.5*: www.un.org; *Figure 3.6*: IRC International Water and Sanitation Centre; *Figures 3.7a, b*: The 3rd World Water Forum; *Figure 3.8*: The 3rd World Water Forum; *Figure 3.9*: Dialogue on Water, Food and Environment.

# Chapter 4

## Table

*Table 4.1, Table 9.6*: Newson, M. (1997) 2nd edn. *Land Water and Development, Sustainable Management of River Basin Systems*. © 1997 Malcom Newson. Routledge. Reproduced by permission Taylor & Francis Books Ltd; *Table 4.2*: Sullivan, et. al. (2002) 'Data selected as WPI component...', Using the Water Poverty Index to monitor progress in the water sector, CEH Wallingford.

## Figures

*Figure 4.1*: H. Reece 1997 ICCE; *Figure 4.2 left*: Louise Oeben/Swynk; *Figure 4.2, middle and right*: Mark Edwards/Still Pictures; *Figure 4.3, left*: Martin Struijf/Swynk; *Figure 4.3, middle*: Associated Press Ltd; *Figure 4.3, right*: Sherwin Crasto/Associated Press; *Figure 4.4*: Clayton, A. M. H., and Radcliffe, N. J. (1996) Sustainability A Systems Approach. Reproduced by permission Kogan Page/Earthscan; *Figure 4.5, left*: Tom Skitt/ICCE; *Figure 4.5, middle*: Mark Boulton/ICCE; *Figure 4.5, right*: Dr Caroline Sullivan/CEH; *Figure 4.6*: International Rivers Network; *Figure 4.7*: Sandrine Simon/Open University; *Figure 4.8*: Robert Gill/Papilio Library; *Figure 4.11*: Len Abrams, The Water Page, www.thewaterpage.com; *Figure 4.12*: Newson, M. (1992) Land Water and Development, Sustainable Management of River Basin Systems. 2nd edn. Reproduced by permission, Thomson Publishing Services; *Figure 4.13*: The Working for Water, programme. Annual Report 2001/2.

Every effort has been made to locate all copyright holders, but if any have been overlooked, the publishers will be pleased to make the necessary arrangements at the first opportunity.

# Index

Entries in **bold** are key terms. Page numbers referring to information that is given only in a figure, table or caption are printed in *italics*.